Catapult Design, Construction and Competition

and

The Projectile Hurling Engines of the Ancients

With forward by Ron Toms

Published by RLT Industries, Inc.

Published by RLT Industries, Incorporated
PO BOX 831085
San Antonio, TX. 78283

For more information, visit http://www.RLT.com

ISBN 0-9776497-0-9

Printed in the United States of America

Give a man a fish and you feed him for a day. Teach a man to fish and you feed him for a lifetime.

Chinese Proverb

Man's mind, once stretched by a new idea, never regains its original dimensions.

Oliver Wendell Holmes

Science is organized knowledge. Wisdom is organized life.

Immanuel Kant

The reasonable man adapts himself to the world; the unreasonable one persists in trying to adapt the world to himself. Therefore, all progress depends on the unreasonable man.

George Bernard Shaw

The important thing is not to stop questioning.

Albert Einstein

We know next to nothing about virtually everything. It is not necessary to know the origin of the universe; it is necessary to want to know. Civilization depends not on any particular knowledge, but on the disposition to crave knowledge.

George Will

The most wasted of all days is one without laughter.

e e cummings

Quotes seen on the Catapult Message board on the Internet:

Fear not, for there are many who feel the same need as you to hurl, and by sticking together we can share information, opinions and adventures. Others might call this a "support group", but little do they know that we are actually advancing our cause, not seeking relief from it.

When life gives you lemons, hurl 'em right back at life's face!

I've noticed a problem with building trebuchets..... You always want to build another, bigger, one.

Plan well, build thoughtfully, and destroy your target safely.

It's not what you hurl, but the hurl itself that matters.

Contents

Section One

Forward

Ron L Toms
Proprietor, www.CatapultKits.com and www.TheHurl.org

"Why would anyone ever need a catapult?" is a question I've heard many times since I started my catapult kit business. The catapults actually fill a very important need. I hear it over and over from teachers and parents alike, "nothing has inspired the kids to learn physics and engineering- even math, more than the catapult project we did." I believe them too because, as a kid, the catapults and other projectile toys I made and played with were instrumental in helping me develop an interest in engineering, physics and the laws of nature. They also gave me a hands-on understanding of basic physics that definitely put me ahead of the class in high school and even later in college.

Catapults and trebuchets are becoming an increasingly popular tool used in teaching engineering concepts and principles of physics. One teacher confessed to me "The trebuchet is the perfect platform for teaching the fundamentals of physics and engineering. Nothing else even comes close." Not only that, but catapult and trebuchet projects lend themselves to inspiring competitive challenges too.

Competitions are popping up everywhere from schools to public festivals, and keen-eyed youths are discovering a great way to have fun, be competitive and learn something about science and history as well. The kids have to learn the math so they can tune and improve their machines. Longer shots win the competitions, and are just more fun! The math is not trivial either. Kids have to analyze the efficiency of the trebuchet and the path of the projectile to improve its range. Over the years, some of these kids have been so fascinated with the creative challenge and exhilarating results of these projects that they've decided to pursue engineering and other technical fields in college.

Getting kids excited about math and science is important to me, and in no small way it's why I'm in this business. When I was in engineering school, it was sad how many of my classmates had no idea how to build a simple mechanical linkage, or use miscellaneous parts to create a solution to a problem. I chalked it up to a lack of experience and creativity on their part. It's unfortunate that a budding mechanical engineer is expected to take a year or two of calculus in high school, but he isn't expected to have any real-world experience in building or working with machines of any kind. In most schools these days, he doesn't even have the option to take a shop class where he can learn to run a bead of weld, or turn the cranks on a mill and otherwise apply all of the stuff he learned in geometry and trig. Where's the fun that inspires the kids to learn and create?

Constructing and tuning a trebuchet or catapult is a perfect way to convert information learned in the classroom into real knowledge about the physical world. Taking the step from memorizing information to actually understanding concepts is much simpler when those concepts take on tangible, three-dimensional form. Do you remember the story of the guy who got into the bathtub and exclaimed "Eureka!" on discovering a way to measure density, or of how the laws of gravity and motion fell into place in Newton's mind when he saw an apple drop from a tree. The trebuchet and catapult projects are simple to build and operate, but to work well they require attention to basic engineering concepts too, but most of all they're fun to shoot! When a kid builds one of these projects with his own hands, and loads his little homemade machine with a golf ball or baseball, then pulls the trigger and sees that machine hurl the ball farther than he (or even most adults) can throw it, suddenly the kid realizes that a little math and engineering can produce real power. He can see the results with his own eyes- it's not just theory anymore, he understands it, and he gets excited! The first thing most people want to do after building and shooting one of these machines is design and build a bigger one!

It's not just a "guy thing" either. We get lots of parents who talk about how their daughters are fascinated with the machines, and how she now takes her math and science classes more seriously.

Why all this interest in getting kids to study math, science and engineering? Because it's important to our society, and it's great mental cross training regardless of what field of work the kids eventually go into. Most people develop a sense for what they want to do in life while they are still in high school or even earlier. A catapult project gives them a chance to see that science and engineering really can be fun, and it's a lot more than just numbers on paper. The real payoff for an engineer is in the field, where she can see, and enjoy the results of her ingenuity. And it may seem counterintuitive, but engineering projects not only help kids learn math and science, they are also great at getting kids back outdoors, away from the massive over-exposure to video games, TV and the Internet.

The world needs good engineers and scientists because, when you really think about it, everything that makes our lives modern- all the machines, technologies, materials and systems that separate us from a minimal hunter/gatherer tribe, all had to be invented, designed or engineered by someone. All progress, all innovation and the myriad things that make life easier, safer, more fun and more productive, all required a spark of creativity, an interest in how things work and how to improve them. The people who do these things have made our modern lives possible.

The pages of these books contain far more information than I had as a kid, when I set out to design and build my first catapult. That was before the Internet, and a short article in an old, dusty encyclopedia in a small school library was my only resource. Thanks to the Internet, and a community of people interested in preserving the art and science of these ancient hurling machines, I found these two rare, out-of-print books, and I decided that they were important enough to reproduce for today's audience. The books may be old, but the science and human drama are still valid. They're not great literature, but they are interesting, and the story of one girl- Mary Hyde, is particularly inspiring. As a sophomore in high school, Ms. Hyde set out to do nothing less than design and construct the largest catapult in the world. It was a struggle, and took several attempts and a lot of study, but with perseverance and a brilliant methodology, she eventually succeeded. How she did it, and her amazing results are the real story.

Today's kids have a wealth of opportunity for achieving similar greatness in their lives, all they need is a spark. Hopefully, some of those kids will even develop a lifelong love for science, reason and creativity, and perhaps even ask the questions that eventually lead to whole new technologies, which ultimately benefit us all.

WARNING!

It is truly unfortunate for all of us that we live in a litigious society that discourages people from being responsible for themselves, such that people like me, who truly wish to share what we know and help others to learn too, are either driven to keep to ourselves or forced to take the risk that these legal disclaimer notices will be effective.

Whatever its perceived purpose or efficacy, the following disclaimer is real.

I am not a professional engineer. I did study mechanical engineering briefly in college, but switched to another discipline in my second year. I am not certified or licensed as an engineer, professional or otherwise, anywhere. I cannot say whether the projects in these books are safe, dangerous or potentially deadly. If you intend to pursue any projects described, outlined, suggested, or pictured in this book, or otherwise inspired by the contents of this book, you do so entirely and strictly at your own risk.

This book is offered for sale to the reader on the condition that it is agreed by any purchaser, and by all readers, that making or operating any device mentioned, pictured or otherwise suggested in this book is potentially extremely dangerous, and that any mishaps, including but not limited to injuries of any nature and severity incurred in the building, operating or otherwise manipulating any device alluded to by or in this book, whether by default or design, shall be wholly and solely the responsibility of the individual reader.

It is advised that before you begin any project of this nature that you consult with a professional engineer, qualified carpenter, welder, and/or any other professional experts relevant to the project you intend to pursue, as related to scale, materials, energy, projectiles, range, and any other qualities of your project.

This book may include technical or other inaccuracies or typographical errors. Ron Toms and RLT Industries, including its agents, owners, officers or affiliates assume no liability whatsoever for errors or omissions in this book. Ron Toms and RLT Industries reserve the right to make changes at any time.

If you do not agree with this, then please put this book down and go find something else to do. (No offense intended!)

A Brief History of Hurling
Ron L. Toms

Hurling, the art and science of projectile throwing, has been around for at least 3000 years. Most cultures developed some form of sling, atlatl, or other simple hand-powered flinging device. The Chinese, who seem to have been the first at so many things, are usually credited with the invention of the first hurling machines too. Around 800 to 1000 BCE the Chinese apparently modified an even more ancient irrigation device known as a Shadouf into a hurling machine that could combine the efforts of several men into a single projectile.

The Shadouf is a counterweighted lever for raising water out of one irrigation ditch and into another. By replacing the bucket with a sling, and replacing the counterweight with several ropes for pulling (one rope for each man) the shadouf could easily be converted into a powerful weapon that today is commonly called a "traction trebuchet".

Around 400 BCE (or earlier) the Greeks invented the Ballista, a two-armed crossbow-like device that used twisted ropes made from hair or sinew for power. A smaller version was called the Scorpio.

A few centuries later, the Romans appear to have simplified the Ballista into a one-armed machine they nicknamed the Onager, more generally known as the Mangonel. Mangonel is a word meaning "Engine of War" and onagers are a wild donkeys with a temper, that tend to buck and kick rocks at anything they find threatening.

Mangonels were used right up until the development of gunpowder and the Cannon. In fact, some historians think the word "gun" was a short form of the word "Gonnel" which was an early type of cannon, and "Gonnel" was likely a shortened form of "Mangonel", since the Gonnel was machine of war. (Just as we say "Plane" instead of "Airplane"). And if you've been in the military, you probably know that a gun isn't something you can hold in your hands. Guns are what they tow behind a truck or build into the hulls of battleships. In other words, heavy artillery!

Although they were still around, Mangonels declined in use when the Trebuchet was brought to the West from the Middle East, around 900 to 1000 AD. Early trebuchets were simple machines powered by men pulling ropes, but in the Western tradition, bigger is typically synonymous with better, and the machines were upsized. Manpower was not sufficient to launch truly enormous boulders, so massive counterweights were employed to drive the machine.

The biggest Trebuchets were said to hurl horse carcasses and other weighty projectiles over castle walls to induce great terror in the defenders. Their reputation was so great that in 1301, King Edward the First of England only had to begin construction of a giant trebuchet named WarWolf outside Stirling Castle to cause the surrender of their army.

Shortly after that, gunpowder and the cannon became the preferred form of artillery, and the catapults were discontinued. During, and after the Renaissance there were a few artists and architects who maintained an interest in the catapults, but their works are as more fanciful than factual. There are also stories of trebuchets being built by Cortez in the battle for what is now Mexico City, and even later by Napoleon.

It wasn't until the late 1800s when an English Nobleman began to research, and experiment with models of these ancient machines, that the resurrection of the catapults as an object of study really began. This time, the catapults were not being built as weapons of war, but as an academic project. Sir Ralph Payne-Gallwey wrote a book about his research in 1907, titled "The Projectile Throwing Engines of the Ancients."

The book wasn't perfect, but it was the best resource available on catapults and trebuchets since ancient times, and it had a lasting effect. Only sixty years later, in 1967, a professor named Bernard Barcio challenged his Latin class to a project- build a catapult. That challenge turned into a national competition that lasted more than a decade and achieved mainstream media recognition. In 1978 Dr. Barcio retired and wrote his book on the subject, "Catapult Design, Construction and Competition."

Less than ten years after those competitions, the event known as "Punkin Chunkin" was born in rural Delaware. Punkin Chunkin is a "sport" that has attracted international attention in television, magazine and Internet publications. More than a hundred competitors apply for a spot on the firing line each year to see who can hurl a ten-pound pumpkin the farthest, and more than forty thousand spectators showed up in 2005 for the event.

Today there are dozens of pumpkin, canned meat-products, turnips, fruitcake, watermelon, and other odd hurling events scattered around the country. In schools, the Science Olympiad has an annual challenge called "Storm the Castle" in which kids are instructed to design and build a catapult or other hurling device for competition.

In February 2000, Ron Toms sold his first trebuchet kit on www.Trebuchet.com as a science project kit for school kids. It was a simple PVC-pipe trebuchet that was so popular that RLT Industries expanded, and now manufactures a dozen different catapult designs, computer simulators, plans, books, videos, CDs and more, and operates five web sites dedicated to catapults, including Trebuchet.com, Mangonel.com, CatapultKits.com, TrebuchetPlans.com and TheHurl.org.

In the hundred years between Payne-Gallwey's pivotal book and this writing, interest in the catapults as an academic teaching tool, and as a recreational hobby has only grown. From the obscure pages of dusty old history books, to nationally televised events and annual scholastic competitions. More than a dozen TV specials have been produced about catapults on Cable TV between the years 2000 and 2005, and more than one businessman has mentioned the possibility of a catapult-based theme park.

Wouldn't that be interesting?

Section Two

Bernard F. Barcio

CATAPULT

DESIGN, CONSTRUCTION

&

COMPETITION

Pompeiiana, Inc.

The Center for the Promotion of Classical Studies

Indianapolis, Indiana

pro
uxore amanda
LILLIAN
et amicis
DAVID LEVE
DAVID DORTCH
NANCY MACK
MARY HYDE

Special thanks go to the following for the use of their photographs:
Mary Sue Best, Jeff Donnella, Mr. & Mrs. Carl Dortch,
Bob Hubbard, Gary Scheffler, and James A. Young.
(Credit is noted beneath each of their photographs)

All other photographs used in this work were donated anonymously to
Pompeiiana, Inc. for use in its publications.

Blueprints of ZEPHYRUS are reprinted by permission of Rick Nolte.

The article and drawings of VESUVIUS are reprinted by permission
of Kurt Rupenthal.

Where quoted, credit is also given to the Red and Black, the student
newspaper of Park School, Indianapolis, IN, and to the Northern
Lights, the student newspaper of North Central H.S., Indianapolis, IN.

CONTENTS

DRESSED IN TRADITIONAL ROMAN MILITARY GARB, AUTHOR
BERNARD BARCIO SURVEYS THE 1973 CATAPULT FIELD
IN INDIANAPOLIS WITH ARMY RESERVE VOLUNTEERS.

INTRODUCTION

The moisture in the night air was just turning to frost as a lone figure walked carefully through the darkness and checked on six huge engines of war. A ray from his lamp fell on the trappings of the machines and he saw that all was ready. On five machines pulleys hung threaded with cable. Tons of counterweight had already been loaded. Long white slings hung limp from firing arms which towered into an overcast sky. He offered words of encouragement to the crew of the dreaded catapult named SCORPIO who would work through the night threading rope through the machine's sides.

There was little left to do except wait. In a few hours a seventh machine would be brought onto the field under the cover of night. Tents were pitched. Standards stood ready to reflect the morning sun.

Suddenly, a commotion at the entrance to the field. A runner reported that the catapult named OTUS AND EPHIALTUS was arriving. Its eighteen-man crew surveyed the field through the darkness, pitched tents and began to round up fire wood to ward off the increasing chill. More cries pierced the night as a zealous wood chopper drove an ax into his own foot and christened the field with blood.

Just before dawn yet another catapult was pulled onto the field. No one got much sleep.

At last the sun rose to reveal a sight that had not been seen for centuries -- a blood-stained field of battle lined with catapults of every description, all fitted, all manned, all aimed at an unseen enemy to the west. One purpose united the crews--victory.

Victory against what? Who was the enemy? Who were these people and why were they manning catapults? The people were twentieth century Latin students who had carefully researched and reconstructed catapults of old in order to participate in the Second National Catapult Contest held, in part, on a ten acre field in Indianapolis, Indiana, on April 14, 1973. Their purpose was to match wits with the most respected geniuses of the ancient world by attempting to rediscover the lost secrets of catapulting. The enemy was the silence of history which had cloaked this most intriguing of past achievements. The wreath of victory would fall to those whose reconstructions most nearly attained ancient distances with rocks and spears, for they would have, for the first time since the Middle Ages, successfully harnessed the natural forces of twisted rope, bent wood and the counterweight.

Such a scene did not really materialize overnight. The project started with the construction of one catapult, named the MARS I, in 1965, and it has led to the construction of over 100 modern catapults entered in the National Catapult Contest. It is the purpose of this book to preserve the science and lore that has arisen from the project and to help and inspire others interested in catapulting.

Bernard F. Barcio, Director
Pompeiiana, Inc., 1978

THE HISTORY OF THE NATIONAL CATAPULT CONTEST

At a routine meeting of the Academic Development Committee of Park School held in December, 1965, the Headmaster urged the faculty to review continuously the content and method of their instruction. He urged them further not to forego unusual methods of stimulating the interest and involvement of students.

Following this meeting, the Latin Master of Park School, Bernard Barcio, reported to his Latin classes that he would assist them in undertaking any project in some way related to Latin. It was then that sophomore David Leve suggested that the Latin II class (thirteen members in all) build an authentic Roman catapult. Another student, Andy SerVaas, brought in a model of such a catapult--having had purchased it in Germany the preceding summer. Another student brought in an out-of-print book on weaponry. It wasn't long before plans were drawn up for an operational Roman catapult.

On subsequent weekends Andy SerVaas, David Leve, Mike Ryan, John Townsend, Geoff Reynolds, Richard Vonnegut, Laurel Woodard, John Katterjohn and Russ Staines met in the basement of the school gymnasium to construct a device capable of hurling a 100 lb rock 100 yards. The source of tension would be a twelve foot long bow consisting of strips of ash, oak and cherry laminated together and tapered at the ends. March 15, 1966, was chosen as the date for the catapult to be officially fired.

As interest in the project flared, the entire school designated Tuesday, March 8, 1966, as Park School's annual rock gathering day--for the purpose of selecting a suitable projectile for the catapult which was named MARS I. The winning rock, a 103 lb granite boulder named "Gaul Blaster", was submitted by the junior class. Russell Staines purchased a large number of buttons bearing the warning "Beware the Ides of March" and was immediately sold out. On Monday, March 14, the second grade demanded the stage to recite a series of original compositions entitled "Odes to a Roman Catapult."

Tuesday, March 15, started out with an oration delivered by Latin student Laurel Woodard to the entire upper and lower school. The oration was titled "An Oration on a Roman Catapult." 3:00 p.m. was scheduled as the "Ides of March Castoff." At that time the entire school body paraded to the athletic field where the Mars I had been set up. Parents and alumni were present. The drum and bugle corp from Marian College lent a military air. Present to cover the firing for the Huntley-Brinkley NBC news team was reporter Pat Trese.

The crowd hushed as Mr. Barcio delivered a Latin pep talk to his students. During a brisk tattoo of drums the order was given to fire. The response to this order was an ominous cracking sound as Gaul Blaster tumbled to the ground setting the first modern catapult record of 3' with a 103 lb rock.

March 15, 1966

On October 1, 1966, the shaken but determined crew of the Mars I travelled to Guelph, Ontario, on the invitation of the 11th Field Artillery Regiment. They were to lead off a Centennial Celebration by firing the Mars I a second time.

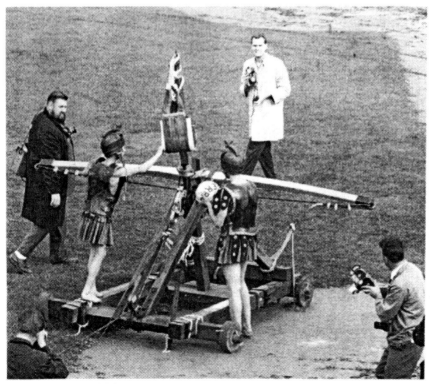

October 1, 1966

Photo above by James A. Young

As the Latin students' interest in catapulting grew, they sent the
following challenge to the Latin department of Culver Military Academy:

PARK SCHOOL

7200 N COLLEGE AVENUE · INDIANAPOLIS INDIANA 46240

TELEPHONE 317·251·1405

MCMLXIX
IDUS NOVEMBRIS

Ludus Parkus Culvero Salutem Dicit.

Provocamini! Venite et vincimini!

Certamen sit iacere saxum pondere

simile quam longissime Romanae

catapultae vero exemplo. Certemus

ante diem tertium Idus Martii

in campo nostro.

Παιδαγογός   Ἀχίλλας   Ἑρμῆς ΙΙ
Διονύσος   Σίσυφος   Ἔναυδρος
Εὐριπίδης   Ἑρμῆς Ι
                Ἱππόκρατης
Οἐδίπος   Ξένων
Ἑρμῆς ΙΙΙ   Αἴρας
Ζεύς   Δημήτριος   Ἔρως
Ἰδιώτης   Πλάτων   Θεόφιλος

Back came a crisp reply from Culver Latin master, John F. Roos:

Vestra provocatio, data Idibus Novembribus, nos tanto pavore
adfecit ut respondere duos mensis non potuerimus, quod in-
telligimus quantam scientiam catapultarum habeatis. Porro, vos
omnes nomina Graeca geritis, et, sicut Laocoon, timemus
Danaos.
Tamen, quia turpe est timere, istam provocationem accipimus,
et vehementer speramus nos posse machinam fabricare quae
fungetur. Sed nobis dicite, precamur: qualis est catapulta qua in
certamine uti debemus?, — cuius modi, speciei, ponderis, mag-
nitudinus? Estne missile re vera sexum, aut nobisne licebit
sagittam proicere? Habetisne in animo veram catapultam? — aut,
fortasse, ballistam aut aliud genus tormenti? Exemplorum
gratia, in libro Jenney's "Second Year Latin", Allyn & Bacon,
in pagina CLXXL, sunt duae picturae, altera catapultae, altera
ballistae. Estne vestra machina similis alterutrique? Suntne
singula (i.e. "specificationes") quae nobis observanda erunt de
fabricatione vel de modo operandi? Vultisne ad nos mittere
picturam vestrae machinae?
Ubi respondebitis, scribite Anglice si optatis, nam quidam e nobis
linguam Anglicam loqui legereque sciunt.

J. F. Ross, magister. JFR
R. L. Griffin, discipulus te praefectus tormentorum.
Culveri, a.d. vii Id. Ian.

On March 14, 1970, the pridie idus Martii, before the whirring cameras of
NBC News, Park School's Latin II class and a contingent from Culver Military
Academy competed in a catapult contest. Reporter John Ramsbottom gave this
account of the encounter in Park School's newspaper, the RED AND BLACK
(March 20, 1970, Vol. L, No. 8, pp. 1 & 2): "True to the 'Ordo Eventum,'
the parade consisting of the armed Latin students of Park, the Culver equites,
the opposing duces (resplendent in their war garb), and a vociferous group
from the far reaches of the empire, moved away from the gym at 3:30. It
immediately encountered a blizzard reminiscent of the worst Gallic winters.
Upon its arrival at the firing site, the acting troupe of Latin II hurried into
its rendition of the death of Caesar. Lance Hamilton was permitted no more
than ten minutes to die, and judging from his continued writhing, he used all
the allotted time. Following on the heels of his final expiration, the Culver
'Rough Riders' presented a display of Roman horsemanship with a few close
calls. But to give them due credit, standing on the backs of two horses
simultaneously cannot be an easy feat to sustain while riding into a twenty-mph
headwind. Promptly at 4:00 David Noling began reading the Latin challenge
to Culver, which was answered by a Culver representative with much tongue-
rolling and addition of syllables. This exchange was followed by the flipping
of a Roman coin, which Park won. Another good omen. At approximately
4:15, Park fired its first shot. ...

"Park's throw of a ten-pound rock exceeded all expectation, being measured
at a stupendous 228 feet. Culver's machine replied (with considerable
difficulty owing to a recalcitrant firing mechanism) with a shot of twenty-
three feet. When their machine was finally unleashed, it nearly decreased
the number of living members of the Culver crew by one."

On January 25, 1971, the following challenge was sent by Park's Latin students
to Mr. Barcio who now taught at North Central High School in Indianapolis:

I·XXV·MCMLXXI

IMPERATORIBARCIOETDISCIPULISLATINISN.C.H.S.

PARCUSTUDORSUPERIORMANUSCATAPULTAEQUESALUTEMDICUNT.

PETIMINIUTINCERTAMINEBALLISTARUMCONTENDATIS.

CERTETURIDIBUSMARTILSINNOSTROAGRO.

SIMILESPROVACATIONESANCULVEREMETADALIAMMANUMSINGULAREM

PARCITUDORISMITTUNTUR.

PROVOCATIONEACCEPTACONDICIONESCERTAMINISCONSTITUENTUR.

VALE

PARCUSTUDORMANUSCATAPULTAE

MANUSPROVOCANS

PLATON	EANDROS
IDIOTES	HERMES I
ACHILLES I	EURIPIDES
OEDIPUS	ZEUS
ESIPUS	ACHILLES II
APPOLODORUS	EROS
HELENA	BENIGRA
SOCRATES	HERMES II
NEMO	ALEXANDROS
GEMINUS	ARISTOTLE

MAGISTRAE

D.COCLEA	A.MINIMEVADUS

MAGISTERCONSILIARIUS

B.ROBUSTUS

PRINCEPS

B.MCCLUSKUS

This contest was described by reporter Steve Wolf in the North Central High School newspaper, the NORTHERN LIGHTS (March 31, 1971, Vol. XV, No. 12, p. 1): "The Ides arrived. Dressed in Roman costumes, the 8th period class paraded across the field. The Latin club was bussed to the scene of the battle to lend moral support, but hundreds of other North Centralites turned out to cheer the team.

"From the start, however, it looked like there wouldn't be much to cheer about. The first shot went backwards, and the crowd gasped as (David) Dortch followed it with a 337' smash of his own. Park-Tudor followed with a modest 47', and North Central again shot--and again flubbed: straight up, straight down. The first volleys set the pace for the remaining rounds, and Dortch's lead was never challenged.

"Pacator, however, (the North Central catapult) provided an ironic twist to the battle. After four mediocre shots in the actual contest, it let loose with a 337' exhibition blast that tied Dortch's newly-set record. Sighed senior Ruthann Tornes, 'I just wish the regular contest could have been as good as the exhibition.'"

The event was again covered by Pat Trese and his NBC news team.

By now interest in catapulting had mounted nation-wide, and Mr. Barcio's Latin students formed a Consilium Catapultarum "to inspire and coordinate a National Catapult Day." The following challenge was issued to schools across the country:

Provocamini

ā Consilio Catapultārum ad catapultārum certamen in quō nonnulli status erunt participes. Construamus catapultās ad saxa jacienda. Catapulta quae saxa jaciet longissimē victor erit.

Certamus Idibus Martii quisque in quoque statū. Respondete si audetis accipere nostram provocationem.

Latin students in Connecticut, Wisconsin and Indiana took up the gauntlet, with Culver Military Academy hosting most of the Indiana competitors. Thus, the First National Catapult Contest sponsored by North Central High School's Consilium Catapultarum, and covered by NBC Chronolog.

By 1974, participation in the contest had grown to such an extent that it could no longer be effectively managed by the Consilium Catapultarum as an extra-curricular activity. When Pompeiiana, Inc. came into being on June 4, 1974, as The Center for the Promotion of Classical Studies, it assumed the sponsorship of the National Catapult Contest and issued the following challenge which was reissued annually until 1978:

PROVOCAMINI A POMPEIIANA AD REIPVBLICAE CATAPVLTARVM CERTAMEN · CONSTRVAMVS CATAPVLTAS QVAE SAXA VEL TELA JACIANT · SINT XII MACHINARVM DIVISIONES ET VIII MISSILIVM CLASSAE · CATAPVLTA QVAE SVVM MISSILE LONGISSIME JACIET VICTOR ERIT IN QVAQVE DIVISIONE CLASSAQVE · SCHOLA QVAE MAXIMAS PALMAS MEREBIT VICTOR REIPVBLICAE CATAPVLTARVM CERTAMINIS ERIT · CERTAMVS QVISQVE IN QVOQVE STATV INTER IDVS MARTIAS ET IDVS MAIAS · RESPONDE SI NOSTRAM PROVOCATIONEM ACCIPERE AVDES ·

As of 1978 there is no longer an official "catapult season." Instead, Pompeiiana, Inc. encourages all students and adults interested in catapulting to try their hand at breaking the records that currently stand. Each successful attempt to set a new world record in catapulting that has been registered with Pompeiiana, Inc. at least two weeks prior to that attempt will be recognized by Pompeiiana, Inc. and included in future catapult record publications.

WINNERS
OF THE SIX NATIONAL CATAPULT CONTESTS
SPONSORED BY
THE CONSILIUM CATAPULTARUM AND POMPEIIANA, INC.
FROM 1972 TO 1977

FIRST NATIONAL CATAPULT CONTEST, 1972

VICTOR: Park-Tudor School, Indianapolis, Indiana

On April 22, 1972, an inscribed plate plus an 80 lb catapult
ball carved from Indiana limestone was presented to David
Dortch whose catapult, ARES II, won the most weight classes.

SECOND NATIONAL CATAPULT CONTEST, 1973

VICTOR: Wayne High School, Fort Wayne, Indiana

On May 19, 1973, a banner was presented to Mrs. Nancy Mack
whose students' catapult, IMPERATOR, earned the most points
(18) based on First, Second and Third Place ribbons won.

THIRD NATIONAL CATAPULT CONTEST, 1974

VICTOR: Wayne High School, Fort Wayne, Indiana

On May 18, 1974, a banner was presented to Mrs. Nancy Mack
whose students' catapults earned the most points (21) based on
First, Second and Third Place ribbons won.

FOURTH NATIONAL CATAPULT CONTEST, 1975

VICTOR: Wayne High School, Fort Wayne, Indiana

On May 17, 1975, a banner was presented to Mrs. Nancy Mack
whose students' catapults earned the most points (24) based on
First, Second and Third Place ribbons won.

FIFTH NATIONAL CATAPULT CONTEST, 1976

Victor: North Central High School, Indianapolis, Indiana

On May 22, 1976, a banner was presented to Mary Hyde whose
school's catapults earned the most points (33) based on First,
Second and Third Place ribbons won.

SIXTH NATIONAL CATAPULT CONTEST, 1977

VICTOR: Wayne High School, Fort Wayne, Indiana

On May 22, 1977, a banner was presented to Mrs. Nancy Mack
whose students' catapults earned the most points (53) based on
First, Second and Third Place ribbons won.

WORLD RECORDS IN CATAPULTING
AND
THE CATAPULTS THAT HAVE SET THEM

Weight of Catapult	Source of Power	Contest Division	Year Set	Catapult	Sponsor	Location	Projectile	Distance
Over 100 lbs	Counter-weight	A	1977	Zephyrus	North Central H.S.	Indpls., IN	10 lb rock	779'6"
			1977	Zephyrus	North Central H.S.	Indpls., IN	20 lb rock	737'
			1977	Zephyrus	North Central H.S.	Indpls., IN	30 lb rock	763'
			1977	Zephyrus	North Central H.S.	Indpls., IN	40 lb rock	798'
			1977	Zephyrus	North Central H.S.	Indpls., IN	50 lb rock	750'
			1976	Zephyrus	North Central H.S.	Indpls., IN	75 lb rock	623'
		B	1976	Hastatus I	Wayne H.S.	Ft. Wayne, IN	1 lb spear	154'
	Twisted Rope	C	1977	Imperator	Wayne H.S.	Ft. Wayne, IN	10 lb rock	554'11"
			1975	Imperator	Wayne H.S.	Ft. Wayne, IN	20 lb rock	369'
			1975	Imperator	Wayne H.S.	Ft. Wayne, IN	30 lb rock	280'11"
			1974	Imperator	Wayne H.S.	Ft. Wayne, IN	40 lb rock	145'5"
			1976	Imperator	Wayne H.S.	Ft. Wayne, IN	50 lb rock	131'
			1974	Imperator	Wayne H.S.	Ft. Wayne, IN	75 lb rock	103'1"
		D	1977	Remus II	Eastwood Jr. H.S.	Indpls., IN	1 lb spear	701'
	Bent Wood	E	1975	Horologium Tintinnabulum	Mauston H.S.	Mauston, WI	10 lb rock	96'8"
			1977	Magnus Ignis	Wayne H.S.	Ft. Wayne, IN	20 lb rock	37'5"
			1977	Magnus Ignis	Wayne H.S.	Ft. Wayne, IN	30 lb rock	24'
			1977	Magnus Ignis	Wayne H.S.	Ft. Wayne, IN	40 lb rock	19'
			1977	Magnus Ignis	Wayne H.S.	Ft. Wayne, IN	50 lb rock	13'5"
			1977	Magnus Ignis	Wayne H.S.	Ft. Wayne, IN	75 lb rock	7'
		F	1974	Deus Jove	Mauston H.S.	Mauston, WI	1 lb spear	438'3"
100 lbs or under	Counter-weight	G	1977	Machina Belli	St. Mary's	Rushville, IN	1 lb rock	191'6"
		H	1976	Hastatus II	Wayne H.S.	Ft. Wayne, IN	1 lb spear	196'
	Twisted Rope	I	1976	Dux Parvus II	Wayne H.S.	Ft. Wayne, IN	1 lb rock	239'
		J	1976	Remus	Eastwood Jr. H.S.	Indpls., IN	1 lb spear	266'7"
	Bent Wood	K	1977	Machina Gigantum	Ben Davis H.S.	Indpls., IN	1 lb rock	186'3"
		L	1974	Rebelorum	Pascagoula H.S.	Pascag., MS	1 lb spear	668'3"

ROCK THROWN THE FARTHEST

A 1977 Zephyrus   North Central H.S. Indpls., IN   40 lb rock   798'

HEAVIEST ROCK THROWN

A 1977 Felix Funditor   Williamson H.S., Williamson, N.Y. 1,400 lbs   8'

THE FARTHEST A 100 lb ROCK WAS THROWN

A 1977 Zephyrus   North Central H.S. Indpls., IN   100 lbs   579'

SPEAR FIRED THE FARTHEST

D 1977 Remus II   Eastwood Jr. H.S. Indpls., IN   1 lb spear   701'

CATAPULT	DIVISION	SPONSOR	LOCATION	PROJECTILE	DISTANCE	YEAR
AENEAS	A	Lyman Hall School	Wallingford, CT	10 lb rock	78'2"	1972
				20 lb rock	75'	1972
				75 lb rock	55'4"	1972
ALBERTUS SORDIDUS	A	Mauston H.S.	Mauston, WI	10 lb rock	31'8"	1972
				20 lb rock	32'8"	1972
AMERICANUS '76	A	Grand Ledge H.S.	Grand Ledge, MI	10 lb rock	110'	1976
ANTERES	A	Park-Tudor School	Indianapolis, IN	10 lb rock	39'	1974
				30 lb rock	67'	1974
APOLLO	K	Roosevelt H.S.	Seattle, WA	1 lb rock	73'5 1/2"	1975
AQUILLA NOBILIS	H	Westlane Jr. H.S.	Indianapolis, IN	1 lb spear	16'9"	1977
ARCULUS	F	Wayne H.S.	Fort Wayne, IN	1 lb spear	178'	1977
ARCUM FRANGETOR	A	Mauston H.S.	Mauston, WI	10 lb rock	34'	1972
ARES II	A	Park-Tudor School	Indianapolis, IN	10 lb rock	583'	1973
				20 lb rock	444'	1973
				30 lb rock	366'6"	1973
				40 lb rock	240'	1973
				50 lb rock	282'	1973
				75 lb rock	188'10"	1973
ARGO I	G	Arvada Sr. H.S.	Arvada, CO	1 lb rock	40'	1973
ARGUS ARBORIS SAXA JACIENTIS	K	North Central H.S.	Indianapolis, IN	1 lb rock	37'7"	1975
ARGUS SAGITARIUS	L	North Central H.S.	Indianapolis, IN	1 lb spear	18'	1976
ARGUS SAXEUS	I	North Central H.S.	Indianapolis, IN	1 lb rock	67'	1976
AUGUSTUS	I	New Haven Sr. H.S.	New Haven, IN	1 lb rock	75'	1973
AURORA NOVA	A	Horlick & Case H.S.	Racine, WI	10 lb rock	139'	1976
BELLATOR	I	Brookhaven H.S.	Brookhaven, MS	1 lb rock	41'7"	1977
BROCKMAN'S WONDED	G	Mauston H.S.	Mauston, WI	1 lb rock	12'4"	1976
CATAPULUS	L	Mount Vernon H.S.	Fortville, IN	1 lb spear	55'11"	1977
CASTOR V	A	Fort Morgan H.S.	Fort Morgan, CO	20 lb rock	91'	1973
CENTURIO I	K	John Glenn H.S.	Norwalk, CA	1 lb rock	75'	1976
CENTURION	J	Mauston H.S.	Mauston, WI	1 lb rock	13'1"	1973
CERBERUS	A	Culver Military Acad.	Culver, IN	10 lb rock	69'1"	1972
				50 lb rock	51'8"	1972
CERTA MORS	I	Fort Hunt H.S.	Alexandria, VA	1 lb rock	21'11"	1975
CHIMAERA	G	Westlane Jr. H.S.	Indianapolis, IN	1 lb rock	75'	1976
CURVUM LIGNUM	K	Brownsburg H.S.	Brownsburg, IN	1 lb rock	73'3"	1976
CURVUM LIGNUM	L	Brownsburg H.S.	Brownsburg, IN	1 lb spear	218'3"	1977
DIANA	J	Roosevelt H.S.	Seattle, WA	1 lb spear	48'	1976
DITIS CERBERUS	F	Mauston H.S.	Mauston, WI	1 lb spear	284'5"	1973
DUX PARVUS IV	J	Wayne H.S.	Fort Wayne, IN	1 lb spear	248'	1977
ENCELADUA II	G	Wheatridge H.S.	Wheatridge, CO	1 lb rock	57'	1973
ERIS	G	Warren Central H.S.	Indianapolis, IN	1 lb rock	69'10"	1976
FACES CAELESTES	A	Fulton Jr. H.S.	Indianapolis, IN	10 lb rock	131'5"	1977
FEROX	K	Mauston H.S.	Mauston, WI	1 lb rock	86'9"	1976
FRANGATOR	K	Mauston H.S.	Mauston, WI	1 lb rock	165'9"	1975
GLADIATOR	G	Wayne H.S.	Fort Wayne, IN	1 lb rock	122'9"	1975
HERACLES	A	Park-Tudor School	Indianapolis, IN	10 lb rock	237'7"	1972
				30 lb rock	132'3"	1972
				40 lb rock	101'	1972
				50 lb rock	53'3"	1972
				75 lb rock	38'5"	1972
HERCULES	D	Bay Sr. H.S.	Bay St. Louis, MS	1 lb spear	110'	1974
HYLUS	A	North Central H.S.	Indianapolis, IN	10 lb rock	371'	1974
				20 lb rock	299'	1974
				30 lb rock	207'7"	1974
				40 lb rock	137'	1973
				50 lb rock	76'	1973
INSUPER	L	Mauston H.S.	Mauston, WI	1 lb spear	92'11"	1976
INVICTUS	C	Portage H.S.	Portage, IN	10 lb rock	119'2"	1972
				20 lb rock	82'9"	1973
				30 lb rock	62'	1973
				75 lb rock	13'	1973
INVICTUS I	C	South Vigo H.S.	Terre Haute, IN	10 lb rock	132'	1972
				20 lb rock	40'8"	1972
JACTURA	G	Brownsburg H.S.	Brownsburg, IN	1 lb rock	114'	1976
LAPIDUM JACULATOR	C	Chardon H.S.	Chardon, OH	10 lb rock	45'3"	1973
				20 lb rock	33'	1973
				30 lb rock	40'3"	1973
LEO PRIMUS	K	Roosevelt H.S.	Seattle, WA	1 lb rock	100'	1977
MACHINA TIGRUM	G	Riverside H.S.	Milwaukee, WI	1 lb rock	137'8"	1975
MAGNUS FIZ	A	North Central H.S.	Indianapolis, IN	10 lb rock	542'	1973
				20 lb rock	485'	1973
				30 lb rock	194'	1973
MAXIMA VIS	C	Miami Springs H.S.	Miami Springs, FL	10 lb rock	35'2"	1974
				20 lb rock	16'	1974
MERCURY I	A	Mishawaka H.S.	Mishawaka, IN	10 lb rock	37'3"	1972
MILES	E	Mauston H.S.	Mauston, WI	10 lb rock	81'5"	1976
MONS COMFORTUS	K	Mount Vernon H.S.	Fortville, IN	1 lb rock	60'6"	1975
NESSUS	I	Brookhaven H.S.	Brookhaven, MS	1 lb rock	100'	1975
NEPTUNE	D	Lakeland H.S.	La Grange, IN	1 lb spear	577'	1975
NOVA CATAPULTA	I	North Central H.S.	Indianapolis, IN	1 lb rock	144'8"	1976

14

CATAPULT	DIVISION	SPONSOR	LOCATION	PROJECTILE	DISTANCE	YEAR
NUMERARE DE AD VOLUPTARIA	C	Black River Falls H.S.	Black River Falls, WI	10 lb rock	36'9"	1975
				20 lb rock	18'2"	1975
				40 lb rock	9'1"	1975
NUNTIUS MORTIS	F	Wilmington H.S.	Wilmington, OH	1 lb spear	80'	1974
ORBITAS	F	Wayne H.S.	Fort Wayne, IN	1 lb spear	276'	1977
OTUS & EPHIALTUS	A	Battle Ground Academy	Franklin, TN	75 lb rock	52'	1973
				335 lb rock	43'	1973
PACATOR	A	North Central H.S.	Indianapolis, IN	10 lb rock	310'10"	1973
				20 lb rock	231'6"	1973
				30 lb rock	195'	1972
				40 lb rock	208'9"	1973
				50 lb rock	165'	1973
				75 lb rock	115'7"	1973
PANTHERA	I	Seattle Prep School	Seattle, WA	1 lb rock	24'6"	1974
PANTHEREUS LAPIDATOR	C	Miami-Palmetto H.S.	Miami, FL	10 lb rock	53'	1973
				20 lb rock	42'	1973
PAULUS	L	Mt. Vernon H.S.	Fortville, IN	1 lb spear	34'	1976
PEGASUS	F	Brownsburg H.S.	Brownsburg, IN	1 lb spear	294'2"	1977
PERENNIS I	I	Westlane Jr. H.S.	Indianapolis, IN	1 lb rock	168'	1975
PETROBOLAS	A	Wilmington H.S.	Wilmington, OH	10 lb rock	541'3"	1974
				20 lb rock	537'	1974
				30 lb rock	453'	1974
				40 lb rock	418'	1974
				50 lb rock	403'	1974
				75 lb rock	237'4"	1974
PILA IGNIS	K	Wayne H.S.	Fort Wayne, IN	1 lb rock	170'6"	1977
PILACTOR	F	Warren Central H.S.	Indianapolis, IN	1 lb spear	167'	1974
PHOENIX	A	Taunton H.S.	Taunton, MA	10 lb rock	91'	1973
PHOENIX I	G	Park-Tudor School	Indianapolis, IN	1 lb rock	82'9"	1974
PLUTO I	A	Mauston H.S.	Mauston, WI	10 lb rock	40'1"	1973
				20 lb rock	32'	1972
PLUTO II	H	Mauston H.S.	Mauston, WI	1 lb spear	84'5"	1974
PLUTO III	B	Mauston H.S.	Mauston, WI	1 lb spear	63'3"	1975
PLUTO IV	L	Mauston H.S.	Mauston, WI	1 lb spear	148'5"	1974
PSEUDOLUS I	A	Mauston H.S.	Mauston, WI	10 lb rock	68'6"	1975
QUINTUS ARIUS	I	Mauston H.S.	Mauston, WI	1 lb rock	89'6"	1974
REGINA LATINA	A	Northeastern H.S.	Fountain City, IN	10 lb rock	50'5"	1975
REX PARVUS	I	Williamson H.S.	Williamson, N.Y.	1 lb rock	133'3"	1977
ROMULUS	G	Eastwood Jr. H.S.	Indianapolis, IN	1 lb rock	181'10"	1975
SAEVITIA	K	Wayne H.S.	Fort Wayne, IN	1 lb rock	80'3"	1975
SANGUINARIUS	C	Brookhaven H.S.	Brookhaven, MS	10 lb rock	98'	1975
				20 lb rock	38'	1975
				30 lb rock	39'	1975
				40 lb rock	36'	1975
				50 lb rock	30'	1975
				75 lb rock	15'	1975
SARPEDON	A	Overton H.S.	Nashville, TN	40 lb rock	175'	1974
				50 lb rock	226'	1975
				75 lb rock	174'8"	1975
SATURN X	C	Mauston H.S.	Mauston, WI	10 lb rock	23'8"	1974
SAXUM	G	Wayne H.S.	Fort Wayne, IN	1 lb rock	64'	1977
SAXUM GRAVISSIMUM IACTATUM	A	Mauston H.S.	Mauston, WI	560 lb rock	3'9"	1974
SCAEVOLA	A	Mauston H.S.	Mauston, WI	393 lb rock	6'2"	1973
SCORPIO	C	Eastwood Jr. H.S.	Indianapolis IN	10 lb rock	104'2"	1975
				20 lb rock	59'10"	1975
				30 lb rock	49'5"	1975
				40 lb rock	36'10"	1975
				50 lb rock	27'8"	1975
SEBENALIS	A	Andrew Jackson H.S.	South Bend, IN	5 lb rock	21'6"	1972
SPARTANIA	A	Laurel H.S.	Laurel, IN	10 lb rock	176'	1972
SPIRO	A	Park-Tudor School	Indianapolis, IN	10 lb rock	127'	1972
				30 lb rock	159'6"	1972
				40 lb rock	90'	1972
				50 lb rock	80'	1972
				75 lb rock	32'	1972
STANLIUS UNUS	E	West Albany H.S.	Albany, OR	10 lb rock	57'7 1/2"	1973
				20 lb rock	32'7"	1973
				30 lb rock	13'8"	1973
STELLA SOLA I	G	Bonnibar Private School	Houston, TX	1 lb rock	85'8"	1973
STELLA SOLA II	G	Bonnibar Private School	Houston, TX	1 lb rock	64'5"	1974
STIRPS MALORUM	A	Edina West H.S.	Edina, MN	75 lb rock	176'1"	1973
T.R.S.H.	D	Great Mills H.S.	Great Mills, MD	1 lb rock	27'6"	1974
TERROR INFERORUM	K	Mauston H.S.	Mauston, WI	1 lb rock	18'1"	1974
TITANUS	A	Mauston H.S.	Mauston, WI	10 lb rock	28'6"	1972
TORMENTA II	A	North Knox H.S.	Edwardsport, IN	10 lb rock	57'10"	1973
				20 lb rock	60'	1973
TORQUEATOR	D	Hattiesburg H.S.	Hattiesburg, MS	1 lb spear	179'8"	1975
URSUS I	C	St. Ignatius H.S.	Cleveland, OH	10 lb rock	32'6"	1974
				20 lb rock	7'2"	1974
VESUVIUS	A	Ben Davis H.S.	Indianapolis, IN	10 lb rock	186'	1977
				20 lb rock	340'	1977
				30 lb rock	246'	1977
VINDEX	J	Roosevelt H.S.	Seattle, WA	1 lb spear	40'6"	1974

THE RECORD SETTERS

While there is no doubt that catapults were among the earliest machines of war and the most sophisticated weapons devised in antiquity, there is a great deal of doubt about the details of their construction and their actual range and capabilities.

From what can be told from references to these machines in Greek and Roman writings, they came in a great variety of sizes and purposes. If we can believe the Roman author Vitruvius, however, they all shared one common detail of construction and design. That is, every catapult built was designed around the length or weight of the projectile it would fire. Unlike the catapults built for competition in the National Catapult Contest, ancient catapults were never intended to fire more than one kind of projectile each. In other words, a catapult designed to fire a twenty pound rock would never be loaded with a seventy-five pound rock or vice versa.

Exaggerated stories about the capabilities of ancient and medieval catapults have come down in history, and it might very well be that a single machine was built at one time or another that, in fact, did perform the feat reported. To believe, however, that it was common for ancient catapults to hurl 500 lb boulders 500 yards would be folly. Nor did every medieval trebuchet have the ability to hurl one ton horse carcasses over forty foot high walls that stood some one hundred yards away.

The real problem, then, is to decide what was the average range of the typical machine built by the average engineers during a routine military operation.

Mr. David Dortch, winner of the First National Catapult Contest, believes that ancient catapults must have been able to be fired safely from beyond the bow range of the enemy. While this is a logical assumption, the next problem is to decide just what was the bow range of the enemy. Again, ancient records offer little help with this problem. We do know that the capability of the bow and arrow was not fully developed by the mediterranean countries nor was it fully developed in ancient times. David suggests that ancient archers could normally fire an arrow with accuracy close to 300 yards. Others believe that a more standard range was closer to 300 feet.

We do know that some of the catapults built during the National Catapult Contest, albeit smaller than their ancient predecessors, have successfully fired spears and 40 lb rocks close to the 300 yard range. But could it be that modern catapultors are actually outdoing the ancients with lesser machines?

The controversy will be left unsettled, and instead a detailed presentation will be given of four modern catapults which have successfully set modern catapulting records by firing a variety of projectiles over 500 feet.

IMPERATOR

TYPE OF CATAPULT: BALLISTA

CONTEST DIVISION: DIVISION C
                       (Twisted-rope powered machine weighing
                       over 100 lbs)

PROJECTILES: ROCKS WEIGHING FROM 10 TO 100 lbs.

RECORDS SET: 10 lb. ROCK HURLED 554'11" (1977)
                       20 lb. ROCK HURLED 369'   (1975)
                       30 lb. ROCK HURLED 280'11" (1975)
                       40 lb. ROCK HURLED 145'5" (1974)
                       50 lb. ROCK HURLED 131'   (1976)
                       75 lb. ROCK HURLED 103'1" (1974)

ENTERED BY: LATIN STUDENTS, WAYNE HIGH SCHOOL,
                       FORT WAYNE, INDIANA

IMPERATOR

It was early in the 1972-1973 school year when the Latin students of
Wayne High School were encouraged by their teacher, Mrs. Nancy
Mack, to start thinking about entering and winning the National Catapult
Contest. This would be the Second National Catapult Contest and
for the first time a Victory Pennant would be offered to the school
whose catapults earned the most points in the contest. This banner was
destined to go to Wayne High School.

The first decision the group made was to choose a catapult division
that would enable them to earn a maximum number of ribbons with
one machine. They chose not to enter Division A which traditionally
drew a great number of counterweight competitors. They preferred
the more ancient type of catapult, the twisted-rope ballista. Since
victory was uppermost in their minds, they further decided to build
the largest twisted-rope ballista constructed to date in the contest and
to follow the guidelines laid out by the only other modern catapult
builder who documented his work--Sir Ralph Payne-Gallway. In his
book entitled The Crossbow this author carefully describes the
dimensions and hardware for a ballista which he thought would perform
according to ancient specifications.

Wanting to proceed with the utmost care, the group started by building
small table top models of their ballista and by testing the weaknesses and
strengths of each design. When they determined the best general
design, they built a model out of 3" x 3" wood that was 5 feet long.
Test firing this model, they learned of the tremendous pressures
exerted on the sides of the catapult frame when the rope was twisted.
One more model was needed. This would be built out of solid oak
and would have the metal gears called for by Sir Ralph Payne-Gallway.
Further tests were conducted with the final model, and plans were
drawn up for the mighty IMPERATOR.

First came a visit to a local sawmill in Fort Wayne where an order was
placed for two 10' long oak beams cut 12" x 18". These would be the
sides of their catapult. A quantity of other oak pieces were also ordered
according to the general dimensions offered by Sir Ralph Payne-Gallway.

Key to the power of their catapult would be the giant steel gears needed
to twist the skein of rope that would be almost one foot thick. The gears
had to be custom made by the Ajax Tool and Die Company in Fort Wayne.
The 2,500 feet of rope needed to power the catapult also would have to
be special. The group decided to use 1/4" Super 707 Blue Line mountain
climbing rope manufactured by DuPont in Philadelphia, Pennsylvania.
The power generated by twisting this mass of rope in the giant gears
would also put great strain on the firing arm. In fact, several arms broke
before a reliable version was constructed by laminating 1" thick ash boards
into a 7' long arm. Neither could the giant gears be turned with ordinary
tools. Special 6' long wrenches had to be crafted in the school's shop.

When IMPERATOR was finally ready for its first year of official competition, it was time to thread the 2,500 feet of rope through the gears. This is not a quick process as one end is secured to a gear and the balance of the rope is pulled around the opposite gear. This loop is then held tightly while the process is repeated for the next loop. Needless to say, it takes several days to string a catapult with this much rope. As the rope is rather expensive and catapults left outdoors are often prone to vandalism, the crew was forced to camp out next to their machine each night until the machine was completely strung and the day of competition arrived.

On the day of competition, record books were produced; and the crew hoisted the large wrenches to begin tightening the skein of rope. How tightly should the skein be twisted? One ancient author suggests that it should be so tightly twisted that ten men can not pull the firing arm back when the twisting is done. Then the crew began its official shots. The ten pound rock traveled 170'9", the 20 lb. rock went 162'7", the 30 lb. rock was fired 83'7", the 40 lb rock 95'6", the 50 lb rock 85' and the 75 lb. rock went 95'6". The final shot made during this first year of official competition was with a 390 lb boulder. While the machine only tossed the boulder approximately five feet, it did so with no damage to its structure. The machine had passed a final durability test. Further, while the distances achieved were not spectacular, they did earn first place ribbons and a total of 18 points for Wayne High School. These 18 points earned the school the VICTOR pennant for the Second National Catapult Contest.

The Latin students went on to win three more pennants over the next four years as they made their machine set the six records that now stand in this division. They also made the giant ballista hurl a 760 lb boulder 10'2" to win a plaque for the heaviest rock hurled in 1975.

As the machine was fired over the years, the crew made several adjustments to the original design. First of all, they learned that the winch mechanism suggested by Sir Ralph Payne-Gallway was not adequate. This broke during the first year of firing and was replaced by a three ton winch secured to a deadman drilled six feet into the ground behind the machine. In subsequent years the machine was cocked by running a chain from the firing arm to the rear of a tractor or a heavy duty army tow truck. The chain was secured to the firing arm by four to six small loops of 1/4" blue line rope which was sprayed with gasoline and ignited to fire the catapult. The burning-rope firing method replaced the original metal release suggested by Payne-Gallway as this device bent the first time it was used. The crew also removed the cross-piece bumper called for in the Payne-Gallway design as this seemed only to destroy the firing arm each time the machine was fired. The absence of the cross-piece did not affect the firing trajectory of the missiles. The cross-piece was reinstalled temporarily, however, each time the machine was cocked. First the arm was pulled back just beyond the location of the cross-piece, then the cross-piece was put in place and the arm was allowed to rest against it while the chain was reset for the final cocking operation.

After firing IMPERATOR competitively for five years, the crews
of the machine learned just how hard it was to use the giant wrenches
to tighten the rope. Each wrench had to be manned by five or six
students, each struggling for a hand-grip on the wrench handle.
As the gears were tightened after each shot to take up the slack and
stretch in the rope, it was necessary to use both wrenches at one
time to turn a single gear on one side of the machine.

Mrs. Nancy Mack and her husband Phillip, who also served as
adviser to the crew, have concluded that the effectiveness of such
ancient ballistae could not have rested in their ability to be fired
rapidly as this is not the case. Each shot takes at least 20 minutes
to set up and complete. No doubt, effective use of such ballistae must
have depended on having a great number of machines ready for firing
at once. Judging from their experiences, the Macks have concluded
further that ancient ballistae broke down frequently and were either
abandoned or repaired in patch-work style to prop up frame and
structure before getting off one final shot.

Because the best distances achieved by IMPERATOR do not seem to
match such staggering ancient catapult shots as 500 lb boulders being
hurled 500 yards, it may be that its designers were actually mislead
by Sir Ralph Payne-Gallway who, in fact, never constructed a ballista.
Perhaps a better source for the dimensions of an ancient ballista might
have been the Roman author Vitruvius who discusses them in his book
DE ARCHITECTURA (Book X, Chapter XI). Vitruvius wrote that all
ballistae and catapultae are to be constructed in proportions according
to the weight or length of the projectile which is to be thrown by the
machine. The basic unit or module around which a ballista is to be
designed is the size of the openings through which the rope to be twisted
is wrapped. To determine the size of this hole and thus the module for
the whole ballista Vitruvius offers the following Greek guidelines:

Projectile Weight	Diameter of Rope Hole	Projectile Weight	Diameter of Rope Hole
2 lbs	3 3/4"	80 lbs	11 1/4"
4 lbs	4 1/2"	120 lbs	1' 1 1/8"
6 lbs	5 1/4"	160 lbs	1' 3"
10 lbs	6"	180 lbs	1' 3 3/4"
20 lbs	7 1/2"	200 lbs	1' 4 1/2"
40 lbs	9 3/8"	210 lbs	1' 4 1/2"
60 lbs	10"	360 lbs	1' 6"

Vitruvius, however, left no drawings of ballistae, and, while he goes on
to describe their construction in some detail, it is often impossible to
know to which part of a machine he is referring in his description.

HIS FINAL MODEL COMPLETE WITH METAL GEARS AND CONSTRUCTED
NTIRELY OF ROUGH CUT OAK WAS ASSEMBLED AND TEST FIRED PRIOR
O BEGINNING THE CONSTRUCTION OF IMPERATOR. STUDENTS ARE SHOWN
HREADING THE ROPE AROUND THE GEARS OF THE MACHINE.

IMPERATOR

IMPERATOR

ETAIL PHOTO OF THE ROPE-TWISTING GEARS ON THE SIDE OF IMPERATOR

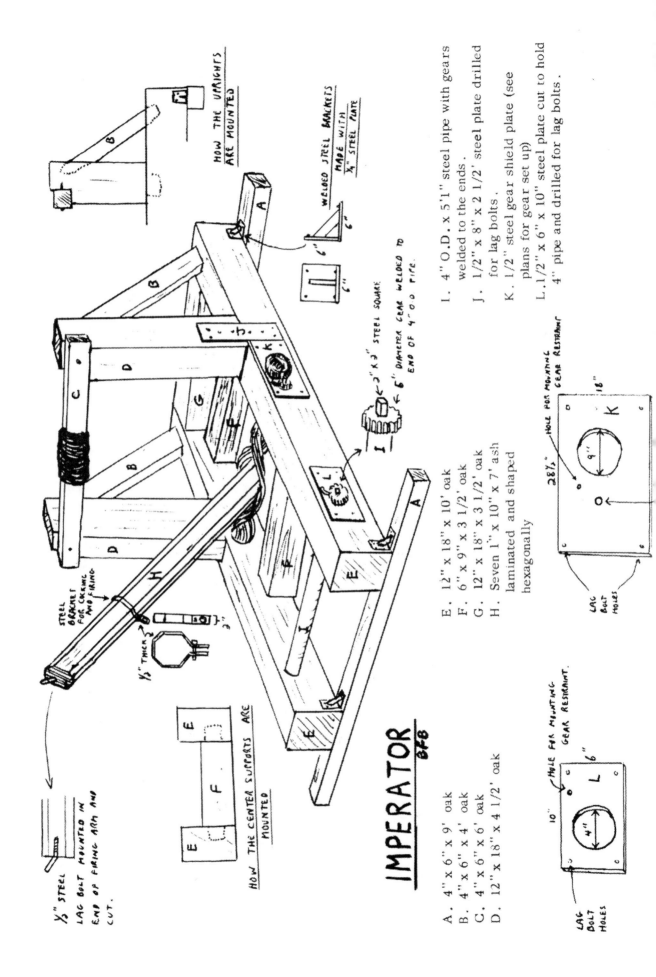

IMPERATOR
BFB

A. 4" x 6" x 9' oak
B. 4" x 6" x 4' oak
C. 4" x 6" x 6' oak
D. 12" x 18" x 4 1/2' oak
E. 12" x 18" x 10' oak
F. 6" x 9" x 3 1/2' oak
G. 12" x 18" x 3 1/2' oak
H. Seven 1" x 10" x 7' ash laminated and shaped hexagonally

I. 4" O.D. x 5'1" steel pipe with gears welded to the ends.
J. 1/2" x 8" x 2 1/2' steel plate drilled for lag bolts.
K. 1/2" steel gear shield plate (see plans for gear set up)
L. 1/2" x 6" x 10" steel plate cut to hold 4" pipe and drilled for lag bolts.

24

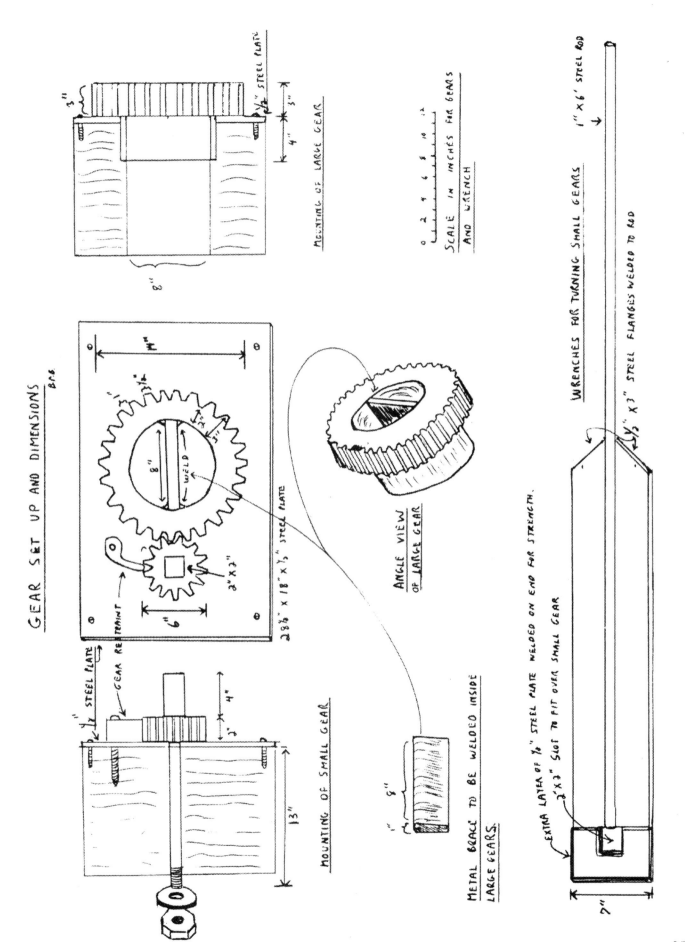

GEAR SET UP AND DIMENSIONS
BNS.

2'8" x 18" x ½" STEEL PLATE

4"

3½"

1½"

8"

WELD

2" x 3"

6"

GEAR RESTRAINT

MOUNTING OF SMALL GEAR

¼" STEEL PLATE

4"

3"

13"

6"

METAL BRACE TO BE WELDED INSIDE
LARGE GEARS.

MOUNTING OF LARGE GEAR

3"

½" STEEL PLATE

3"

4"

8"

ANGLE VIEW
OF LARGE GEAR

SCALE IN INCHES FOR GEARS
AND WRENCH

0 2 4 6 8 10 12

WRENCHES FOR TURNING SMALL GEARS

1" x 6' STEEL ROD

½" x 3" STEEL FLANGES WELDED TO ROD

EXTRA LAYER OF ⅛" STEEL PLATE WELDED ON END FOR STRENGTH.

2" x 3" SLOT TO FIT OVER SMALL GEAR

7"

REBELORUM

Photo by Gary D. Scheffle

TYPE OF CATAPULT:	CATAPULTA
CONTEST DIVISION:	DIVISION L (Bent-wood powered machine weighing 100 lbs. or less)
PROJECTILE:	ONE POUND SPEAR
RECORD SET:	668' 3" (1974)
ENTERED BY:	LATIN STUDENTS, PASCAGOULA H.S. PASCAGOULA, MISSISSIPPI

Steve Levine of Pascagoula, Mississippi, was 16 years old when he
designed his first version of a bow-powered spear hurling catapult.
Working with his advisor, Mr. Ben Levine, and fellow Latin classmates Billy Portas, Billy Baker, Bobby Baker and Greg Harris, he
adopted the goal of constructing a light-weight ballista that could
hurl a one-pound spear farther than the 109' record set in the spring
of 1973.

The catapult would be called REBELORUM and its initial design
called for a 28' long bow constructed of lemon wood. Limited by a
self-imposed $40.00 budget, however, the group decided against
importing lemon wood from South America and settled for Southern
yellow pine instead. Steve Levine designed a spring-leaf type bow
to be made of varying length yellow pine boards specially cut one
inch thick and three inches wide. These would be lashed but not
glued together.

Wood for the catapult was obtained from Porter's Saw Mill in
Escatawpa, Mississippi, and then ripped at Flechas boatyard.
Although the bow was originally intended to be 28 feet long, the
100 pound weight limit on the entire machine made it necessary
to shorten the bow to 20 feet long. The supporting structure was
made of fir, and the whole machine was designed to be easily
disassembled.

After the crew constructed the catapult and its 30 inch long finned
spears, Steve began to practice firing in his own neighborhood.
While the first shot barely made it across the street, Steve soon had
to attach a 135 yard long restraining cord on the spear to avoid
hitting a house at the far end of his street.

Finally, on Saturday, April 14, 1973, the catapult was officially
fired in the parking lot of the football stadium of Pascagoula H.S.
The first of two official shots measured 455'8", and the second
524'8".

Encouraged by their Latin teacher, Mrs. Sharon Gibson, the crew
entered REBELORUM in the 1974 catapult contest and attempted to
break their old record. Anticipating a shot that would exceed the
boundaries of the stadium parking lot used the year before, the crew
obtained permission to fire their catapult on the grounds of the
Pascagoula Airport. It was there in the spring of 1974 that Steve
and his crew set the world record of 668'3" with a one pound spear
fired from a light weight bow powered catapult.

The spear used in setting this record is on display at Pascagoula H.S.

Photo above by Gary D. Scheffler

REBELORUM

DETAILED DRAWINGS

B.F.B.

TOP VIEW DETAIL OF BOW MOUNTING

1/2" x 1" WOODEN STRIPS

METAL BANDS TO SECURE BOW TO RAMP

3/4" X 1" METAL STRIPS

BOW

SPEAR

30" DOWEL ROD - 1" DIAMETER - 1 LB WT.

LOCATION OF FINS

GROOVE FOR SPEAR

1" x 1 1/2" STRIPS

1 1/2" X 3 1/2" X 18' RAMP
(LUBRICATE GROOVE WITH LIQUID SOAP)

BOAT WINCH

45°

1" x 4" x 8' BRACE

1" x 4" x 13' FRONT BRACE

BOW SECTION

BOTTOM SUPPORT 1 1/2" x 3 1/2" x 4'

BLOCKS MOUNTED UNDER BOTTOM SUPPORT TO HOLD FRONT BRACE IN PLACE

FRONT VIEW OF FRONT BRACE

BOW CONSTRUCTION DETAIL

1" X 3" YELLOW PINE LASHED BUT NOT LAMINATED

BOW STRING LASHING

6' LONG

9' LONG

13 1/2' LONG

15 1/2' LONG

30' LONG

BOW STRING LASHING

BOW STRING ATTACHMENT TOP VIEW

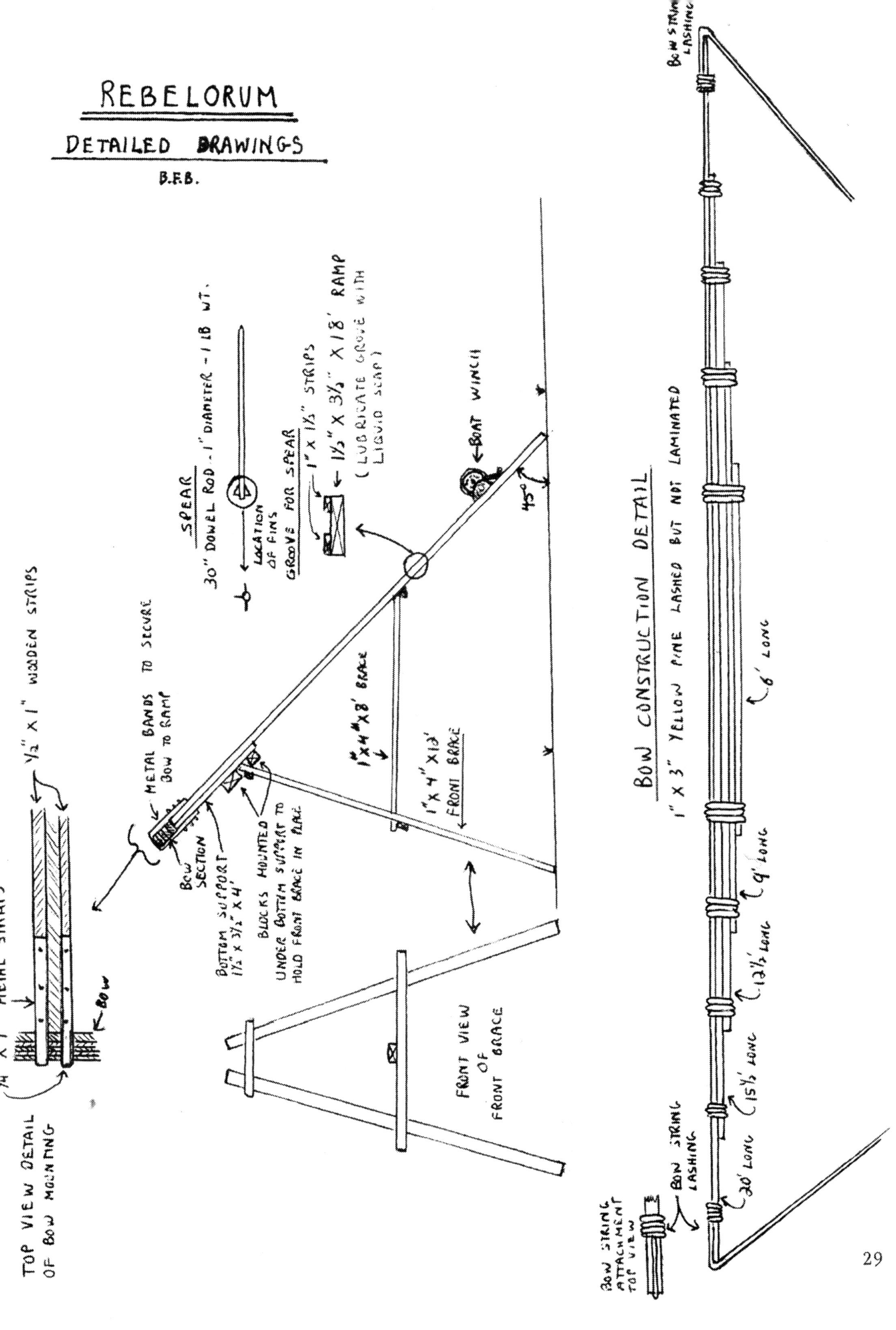

REMUS

TYPE OF CATAPULT:	CATAPULTA
CONTEST DIVISION:	DIVISION D (Twisted-rope powered machine weighin over 100 lbs.)
PROJECTILE:	ONE-POUND SPEAR
RECORD SET:	701'
ENTERED BY:	LATIN STUDENTS, EASTWOOD JUNIOR HIGH SCHOOL, INDIANAPOLIS, INDIANA

REMUS

In 1973 the Archaeology Club at Eastwood Jr. H.S., Indianapolis, elected to construct a pair of catapults named ROMULUS and REMUS and to enter them in the Second National Catapult Contest under the aegis of the Latin I class being taught at Eastwood by Mrs. Maria Nichols. ROMULUS would be a light-weight counter-weight catapult designed to throw one-pound stones and REMUS would be a light-weight twisted-rope machine designed to fire a one-pound spear.

Thus, early in January, 1973, a group of enthusiastic Archaeology Club members met at the home of Janice Myers with their advisor, Mr. Rick Harrison, a member of an Army Reserve unit stationed in Indianapolis. The group had a few general ideas but no definite plans. The Encyclopaedia Britannica was consulted under the heading "Engines of War." Here they found a sketch of a spear-thrower called a "mongonel", and they decided to make this their basic model. Since the group was interested in building a machine that weighed 100 lbs or less, they determined that the heavy base shown in the sketch could be replaced by just enough sub-structure to give the spear ramp the desired 45 degree angle. They also chose not to attempt to reconstruct the windlass shown in the encylopaedia. Instead they would substitute a small boat winch which would be light-weight, inexpensive and safety tested.

Dimensions for their spear thrower were guessed at and some rough working plans were drawn up before the next meeting. A quantity of free hard and soft wood was gathered, and the final dimensions were adjusted to the lumber on hand. Six Saturdays later the machine was complete and ready for test firing.

On April 12, 1973, two days before the official firing of REMUS, the group was asked to give a demonstration of their machine for the history classes at Eastwood. Although the crew had been careful to use steel cable as its "bowstring" for added safety, they had not replaced the nylon rope that came with the winch they had purchased. Unbeknown to them, this rope had frayed during the many test shots, and as they cocked the machine back to load the spear, the rope broke when the machine was at full tension. To the great surprise of all spectators, the catapult fired its steel hook 350 feet down field, brushing the hand of a crew member as it left the machine. By the day of the official contest, Saturday, April 14, the shaken crew had replaced the winch rope with 1/4" steel cable and had adopted new firing procedures to avoid future close calls. An official shot of 183' with a one-pound spear won first place for light-weight twisted-rope spear hurlers during the Second National Catapult Contest.

A new crew took over the machine each subsequent year, finally perfecting a record distance of 266'7" with their light-weight machine in 1976.

In 1977, Kevin Pavey, Mike Kirages, Scott Murphey and George Tikijian, members of Eastwood's Latin I class, decided to redesign REMUS into a heavy-weight machine which they would enter as REMUS II in Division D of the National Catapult Contest. They wanted to make the rope-twisting box heavier so it couldn't collapse under the compression; they wanted to design a more efficient method of twisting the ropes; and, finally, they wanted to lengthen the firing arms and the spear ramp, raising the front of the machine almost six feet into the air.

Success came on Saturday, May 7, 1977, when REMUS II fired its one-pound spear 701' down field to set a new world's record for the farthest spear fired by any modern catapult.

REMUS AS A DIVISION J CATAPULT.

REW MEMBERS PREPARE TO FIRE REMUS II DURING THE 1977 CONTEST.

AS A LIGHT-WEIGHT CATAPULT ENTERED IN DIVISION J, REMUS HAD A SHORTER SPEAR RAMP AND VERY SIMPLE ROPE TWISTING GEAR.

DETAIL OF TWISTED-ROPE FIRING ARM ON REMUS.

DETAIL OF TRIGGER AND WINCH ON REMUS.

REMUS II

-5FB

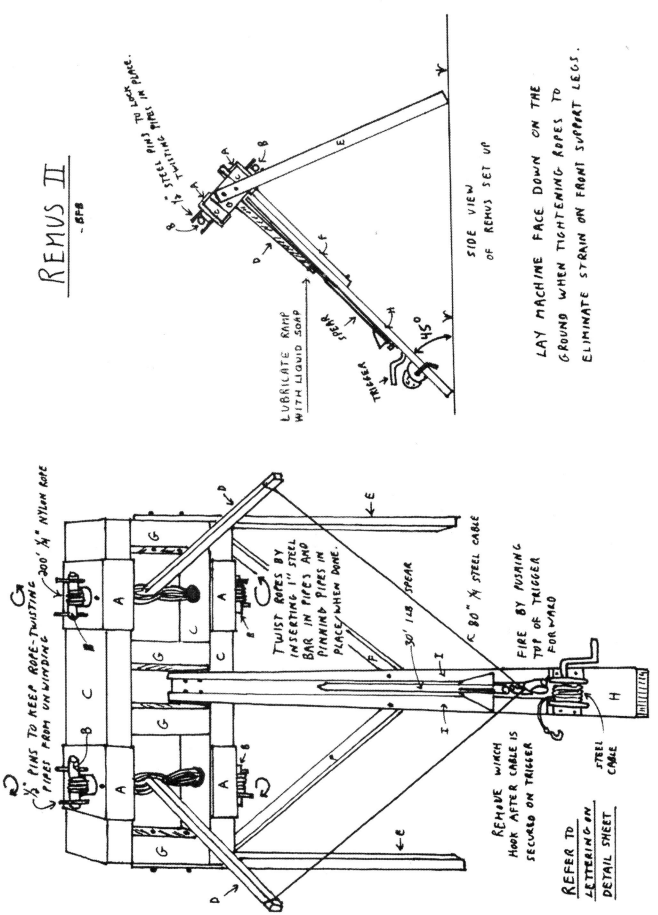

STEEL PINS TO LOCK PIPES IN PLACE.

8 × ½" STEEL PINS TO LOCK — TWISTING PIPES IN PLACE.

LUBRICATE RAMP WITH LIQUID SOAP

SPEAR

TRIGGER

45°

SIDE VIEW OF REMUS SET UP

LAY MACHINE FACE DOWN ON THE GROUND WHEN TIGHTENING ROPES TO ELIMINATE STRAIN ON FRONT SUPPORT LEGS.

200' ½" NYLON ROPE

½" PINS TO KEEP ROPE-TWISTING PIPES FROM UNWINDING.

TWIST ROPES BY INSERTING 1" STEEL BAR IN PIPES AND PINNING PIPES IN PLACE WHEN DONE.

30' 1½ SPEAR

80" ½ STEEL CABLE

FIRE BY PUSHING TIP OF TRIGGER FORWARD

REMOVE WINCH HOOK AFTER CABLE IS SECURED ON TRIGGER

STEEL CABLE

REFER TO LETTERING ON DETAIL SHEET

35

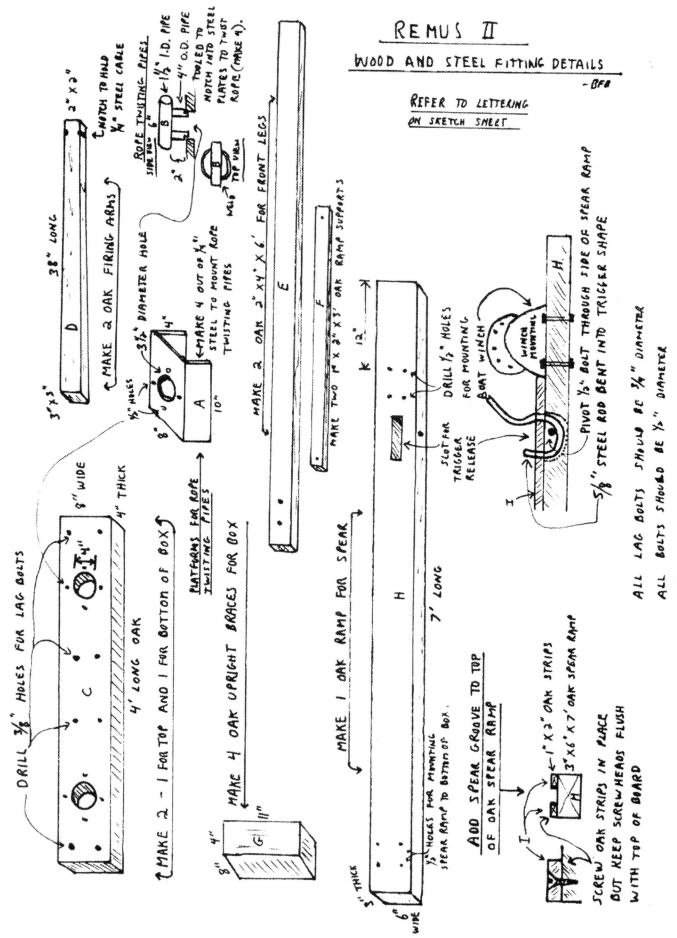

REMUS II

WOOD AND STEEL FITTING DETAILS

— BFB

REFER TO LETTERING ON SKETCH SHEET

2" × 3"

↑ NOTCH TO HOLD ¼" STEEL CABLE

38" LONG

D

3" × 3"

← MAKE 2 OAK FIRING ARMS

ROPE TWISTING PIPES

SIDE VIEW

1½" I.D. PIPE

4" O.D. PIPE

B

6"

DOWELED TO NOTCH INTO STEEL PLATES TO TWIST ROPE (MAKE 4).

2'

TOP VIEW

HOLE

3½" DIAMETER HOLE

4"

A

← MAKE 4 OUT OF ¼" STEEL TO MOUNT ROPE TWISTING PIPES

½" HOLES

8"

10"

MAKE 2 3"×4"×6" FOR FRONT LEGS

E

MAKE 2 OAK 3"×3" OAK RAMP SUPPORTS

F

12"

K

DRILL ½" HOLES FOR MOUNTING BOAT WINCH

SLOT FOR TRIGGER RELEASE

WINCH MOUNTING

PIVOT ⅜" BOLT THROUGH SIDE OF SPEAR RAMP

H

⅝" STEEL ROD BENT INTO TRIGGER SHAPE

I

ALL LAG BOLTS SHOULD BE ¾" DIAMETER

ALL BOLTS SHOULD BE ⅜" DIAMETER

DRILL ⅜" HOLES FOR LAG BOLTS

8" WIDE

4" THICK

4'''

4" LONG OAK

C

MAKE 2 — 1 FOR TOP AND 1 FOR BOTTOM OF BOX

PLATFORMS FOR ROPE TWISTING PIPES

8"

MAKE 4 OAK UPRIGHT BRACES FOR BOX

4"

11"

G

8"

MAKE 1 OAK RAMP FOR SPEAR

7' LONG

H

½" HOLES FOR MOUNTING SPEAR RAMP TO BOTTOM OF BOX

3" THICK

6" WIDE

ADD SPEAR GROOVE TO TOP OF OAK SPEAR RAMP

1" × 3" OAK STRIPS

3" × 6" × 7' OAK SPEAR RAMP

H

I

SCREW OAK STRIPS IN PLACE BUT KEEP SCREWHEADS FLUSH WITH TOP OF BOARD

36

ZEPHYRUS

Photo by Jeff Donnella

TYPE OF CATAPULT:	TREBUCHET
CONTEST DIVISION:	DIVISION A

(Counterweight powered machine weighing
over 100 lbs, and limited to a one-ton
counterweight and a 15 foot distance
from pivot to counter-weight placement.)

PROJECTILES: ROCKS WEIGHING FROM 10 TO 100 lbs.

RECORDS SET:
```
 10 lb. ROCK HURLED 779'6"   (1977)
 20 lb. ROCK HURLED 737'     (1977)
 30 lb. ROCK HURLED 763'     (1977)
 40 lb. ROCK HURLED 798'     (1977)
 50 lb. ROCK HURLED 750'     (1977)
 75 lb. ROCK HURLED 623'     (1976)
100 lb. ROCK HURLED 579'     (1977)
```

ENTERED BY: LATIN STUDENTS, NORTH CENTRAL H.S.
                                INDIANAPOLIS, INDIANA

37

As a sophomore studying Latin at North Central High School in Indianapolis, Mary Hyde conceived the idea of constructing the largest catapult built to date, one which would be capable of the long standing goal of firing a 100 lb. rock 100 yards.

Mary enlisted the aid of her father, David Hyde, as advisor to the project, and was aided by fellow students Rick Nolte and Steve Klotz. During this first year the crew came to realize the full extent of the task they had undertaken. Hours were spent locating used telephone poles and having them transported to the catapult field. Then came the agony of waiting until they were planted properly through the volunteer efforts of the Indianapolis Telephone Company. When the waiting was over and the crew could finally work on the structure, they found that the days were slipping away rapidly. The secret to the future success of ZEPHYRUS was the uniquely designed arm featuring spreaders and cable and closely resembling the mast of a ship. This part of the catapult was built in the backyard workshop of the Hydes and transported piecemeal to the field shortly before the day of the contest. Raising the huge mast-like firing arm into place using only winches and muscle power took time, however, and by the time the machine was ready for its first shot, the day for official catapult competition had drawn to a close.

True to their motto "Ad Astra Per Aspera", Mary and her crew now enlisted the help of Mary Richards, Joe McArdle and Steve Douglas, and they all determined to work over the summer and be sure that ZEPHYRUS would be working at its best the following year. So, while other students frolicked on the beaches, Mary and her crew planned and sweated over their creation.

As anyone who has seriously catapulted knows, there is a great difference between building a catapult and getting it to work to its full potential. It takes practice shot after practice shot. It takes careful, yes scientific, record keeping, it takes hours of studying over photographs and slow-motion movie sequences. With each shot requiring a minimum of 45 minutes to complete and measure, hours were consumed test firing in the seven weight classes in which the catapult would be competing.

The second year of competition arrived and the crew saw their machine fire a 10 lb rock 267'8", a 30 lb rock 103'4" and a 75 lb rock 160'10" --all second place records.

More practice was required. More experimentation with the method of releasing the sling, more testing of sling lengths for projectile weights, and more adjustments of the angle of the slip-pin on which one end of the sling rested.

38

The spring of 1976 arrived. Mary Hyde was now a senior in high school, and she was determined that ZEPHYRUS could and would set first place records in every weight class it entered. After another summer of practice shooting, more weekends spent camping out next to ZEPHYRUS to protect the expensive and sophisticated gear that had been gathered over the years, and scores of carefully documented practice shots in all weight classes, Mary and her crew knew exactly what their battle plan would be. They knew how each shot should be set up. They knew which sling length to use and what the angle of the release pin should be for each weight class. They knew what trajectory to expect for a "good" shot the second the sling would release its projectile.

Other catapults shared the field with ZEPHYRUS, and there was much shouting, hammering and milling about as the day began. But once ZEPHYRUS was ready to be fired, a solemn hush spread over the field. The crowd respected the determination of Mary's crew; they stood in awe of the majesty of a catapult that must surely come close in size to its ancient predecessors. A safety check was made of the down-range field as spotters waited tensely to retrieve the projectile after its distance would be measured. Finally the count-down was given, loud and steady: "One, Two, Three, Fire!" A crew member pulled a rope stretched some 100 feet safely away from the machine, a release hook opened, the huge counterweight began to fall, the firing arm accelerated, the projectile in its sling accelerated on its own course making an eerie "swoosh" through the air, and then came the release of the projectile as all eyes watched it climb steadily in a beautiful arc across the field. Silence--until the rock dove to the ground and struck with a thump that could be felt halfway across the field. Dirt flew straight upwards and a world record had been set--693' with a 10 lb rock.

With its crew laboring straight through until sunset, ZEPHYRUS fired a 20 lb rock 720', a 30 lb rock 735', a 40 lb rock 748'2", a 50 lb rock 710' and a 75 lb rock 623', a record which still stands. Mary would not quit, however, until she had satisfied a goal for which others had tried over the past ten years. She wanted to hurl a 100 lb rock 100 yards. This shot was saved for the end lest the heavy projectile break the firing arm of the mighty machine. But ZEPHYRUS didn't break. In fact, it hurled its 100 lb missile 565'6" down field.

Mary Hyde graduated from North Central High School with a feeling of accomplishment shared only by her crew and their advisor, David Hyde. ZEPHYRUS was to be fired again, however, in 1977. Mary now became the advisor and a new group of North Central students worked with her as the world's largest catapult set the records which now stand for a heavy-weight trebuchet.

THIS PHOTO SHOWS HOW THE HUGE MAST-LIKE FIRING ARM WAS
RAISED INTO PLACE MANUALLY. A TEMPORARY PIPE SUPPORTS
A PULLEY USED TO RAISE THE ARM UNTIL IT REACHES THE PIVOT
HOLES PRE-BORED INTO THE SUPPORT POLES. WHEN THE ARM WAS
RAISED HIGH ENOUGH, AN AXLE PIPE WAS INSERTED THROUGH
THE HOLES AND THE PIVOT PIPE OF THE ARM. THE TEMPORARY
PIPE WAS LATER REMOVED AND A BOTTOM SPREADER WAS ADDED
TO THE FIRING ARM ALONG WITH SUPPORT CABLES. THE TON
OF COUNTERWEIGHT WAS NOT LOADED INTO THE BARRELS UNTIL
THE ARM WAS RAISED AND SECURED INTO PLACE.

ZEPHYRUS

CREW MEMBERS PREPARE TO COCK ZEPHYRUS.

Photos above by Jeff Donnella

ZEPHYRUS

IN 1966 THIS ROCK WAS REJECTED BY THE CREW OF
A CATAPULT NAMED THE MARS I WHEN THE FIRST
MODERN ATTEMPT WAS MADE TO FIRE A 100 lb ROCK
100 YARDS. MARY HYDE HERE LOADS THE HUGE
ROCK INTO THE CANVAS SLING OF ZEPHYRUS BEFORE
IT IS FLUNG 565'6" DOWN FIELD ON THE IDES OF MAY,
1976, EXCEEDING THE 1966 GOAL BY 265'6".

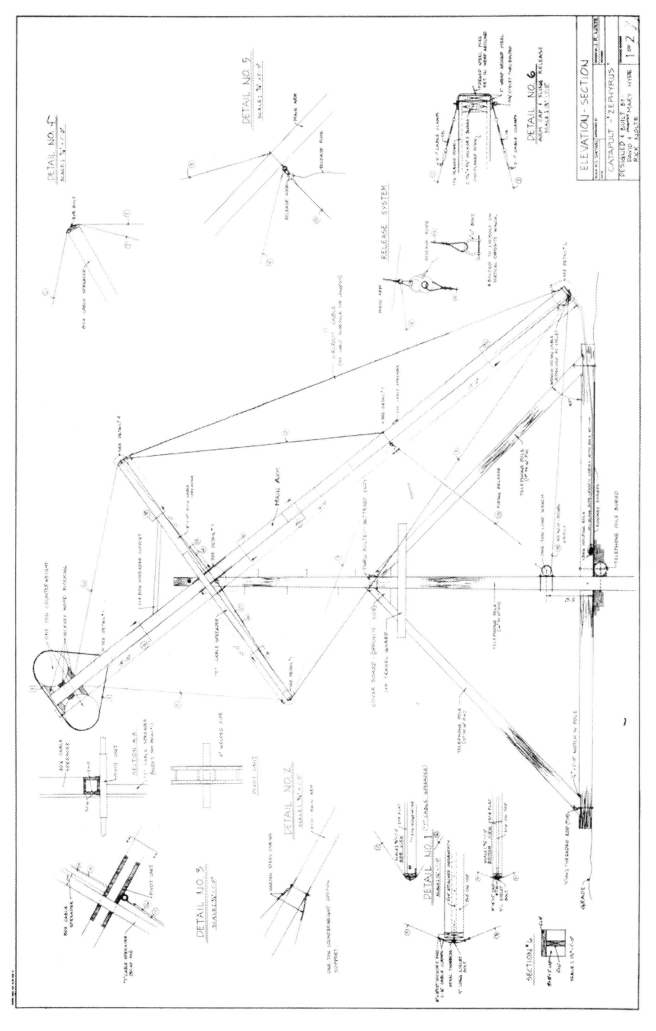

45

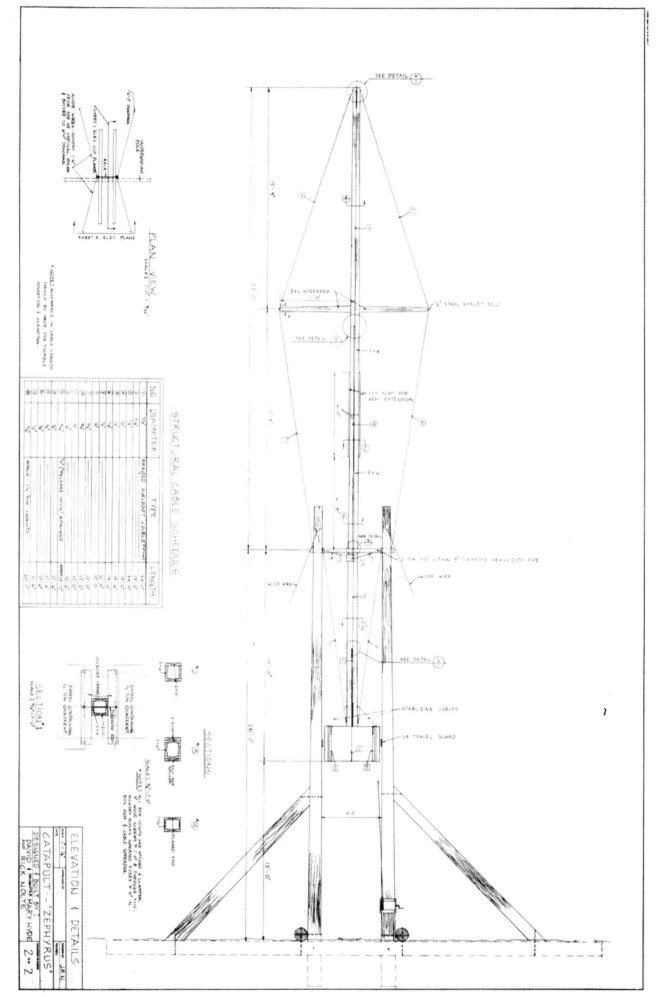

PROJECTILES

In 1972 the crew of another North Central High School catapult,
PACATOR, had a set of "catapult balls" specially turned from
Indiana limestone to the following diameters:

10 lbs	6 1/4"
20 lbs	6 7/8"
30 lbs	9"
40 lbs	10"
50 lbs	10 3/4"
80 lbs	12 1/4"

In setting its records ZEPHYRUS fired the 30, 40 and 50 lb balls
from this set. Field stones were used for the other weight classes.

QUICK RELEASE HOOK

The quick release hook used to fire ZEPHYRUS after the arm was
cocked and the sling was loaded was a #3398 T 2 Automatic Release
Lifting Hook safety tested to 2,500 lbs. It was purchased from the
McMaster-Carr Supply Co., P.O. Box 4355, Chicago, IL 60680.

CRITICAL ANGLES OF THE SLING SLIP PIN AND SLING LENGTH

Key to the release of a sling from the firing arm of a trebuchet is the
angle of a small slip pin which is mounted at the firing tip of the long
arm. The length of the sling is also critical. The following chart
shows what pin angle and sling length were used by ZEPHYRUS in setting
its records:

Rock	Sling length	Pin angle	Distance fired	Year
10 lb	31'6"	9°	779'6"	1977
20 lb	31'6"	12°	737'	1977
30 lb	31'6"	10°	763'	1977
40 lb	31'6"	12°	798'	1977
50 lb	31'6"	12°	750'	1977
75 lb	31'6"	12° - 13°*	623'	1976
100 lb	31'6"	15°	579'	1977

*records unclear.

SETTING THE PIN ANGLE

MEASURING THE SLING

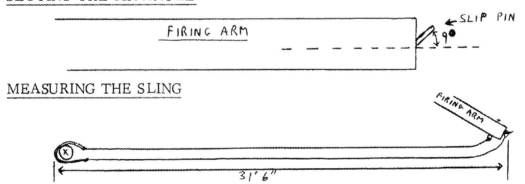

THE STORY OF A CATAPULT NAMED

VESUVIUS

By Kurt Rupenthal

The planning of VESUVIUS began in January of 1977 when two Ben Davis
High School physics teachers helped me design a machine that could
throw a 100 lb rock 700 feet. One calculation followed another. At one
point we thought that a machine 1,200 feet high would be needed! After
many complex calculations a design using a newly designed counterweight
system was finally decided upon. VESUVIUS would not resemble the
trebuchets entered in the National Catapult Contest previously. By using
a large one inch thick nylon rope, the counterweight would be connected
to a huge semi-circular pulley wheel 26 feet in diameter. In this way

the counterweight would have no moment of inertia and, therefore,
be capable of falling with greater speed.

In February I began drawing up some initial plans. Interest was
building among my fellow Ben Davis High School Latin students. Several
money-making projects were underway to finance the project. Friends
offered constant encouragement and unending moral support.

Early in March, my crew and I began rounding up materials for construction.
Telephone poles were our first major concern. Two main poles, already
in position on the catapult field, were designated for our use. Mr. Gerald
Ferguson provided a company-owned flat-bed trailer truck to haul additional
donated phone poles from Indiana Bell. He also provided a 5,000 lb capacity
winch and some cable. Construction was underway. Indiana Bell further
donated twenty 18" bolts, 300 feet of braided strand cable, four anchors,
and many cable clamps. Our first job was to dig the four large holes
needed to erect four main pole braces. Father, brother and friends were
enlisted to help the crew dig.

After the brace poles were in position and bolted, work began on the
construction of the unique firing arm with its 26' diameter semi-circle.
The arm was constructed on the field, about 100 feet from the base of
the catapult. When built, it would be heavy, and we did not want to have
to move it very far. It was built mainly of 2" x 10"s and some old beams
that I had salvaged from a house that had burned down. The arm also had
to be constructed propped up 2 1/2' above the ground so we would have room
to work on its bottom side. After much nailing, drilling, bolting and cutting,
the 3,000 lb arm was ready to be hoisted into position.

The original plans called for a 3" O.D. pipe for the pivot. I was unsure
that this pipe would stand the stress as the main poles of the catapult were
5' 2" apart. My father asked a friend of the family, Mr. Leroy Eckert,
to solve the problem. Mr. Eckert took the design to the stress engineering
department at Detroit Diesel Allison in Indianapolis. The engineers found
that a 3" O.D. pipe would fail under the anticipated load. A 4" O.D. pipe
with a steel reinforced concrete core would, however, stand the stress with
a safety factor of two. Two such pipes were required--one for the actual
pivot, and one to be temporarily mounted 3' above the pivot point in order to
hoist the heavy arm into place. The winch cable was put over the top of
the pipe and attached to the firing arm. After three attempts and two days'
work, the arm was finally lifted into position. We now had only two weeks
before the firing date to complete the catapult.

Finally, the day of the contest came. All was finished except connecting
the guy wires from the rim of the pulley to the pivot. My father, brother and
I started work at 6 a.m. At 1 p.m. we connected the two 55 gallon drums

of concrete to the one inch thick nylon rope. It was now time to fire. The winch began taking up the weight, and slowly the wheel began to bend over sideways at the top, a motion which would cause it to break if not corrected. The weight of the cement-filled barrels being lifted by the giant pulley had caused it to compress to the point that loosened the guy wires we had installed to prevent this tilt. When a turn buckle snapped, it was time to let the counterweight down and adjust all the cables and turn buckles.

On our second attempt to cock VESUVIUS, only one counterweight barrel was used, about 900 lbs of weight. The wheel stayed fairly straight this time. The cocked firing arm was connected to the release mechanism, our sling was attached and loaded with a 10 lb rock. As I pulled the firing cord, I was expecting the worst. To my surprise, it was a beautiful shot that landed 186' down range.

We added more weight to the counterweight and cocked the machine again. A 20 lb rock was fired 340'. More counterweight was added and a 30 lb rock was loaded into the sling. This time, however, the sling opened prematurely when VESUVIUS was fired, and the rock fired nearly straight up. Worse yet, the tip of the firing arm came around and struck the ground in front of the catapult putting a 12' crack in the main board. We had to retire VESUVIUS for the year.

With more design improvements and practice time, we expect to reach our goal of firing a 100 lb rock 700 feet in the near future. We are, after all, the challengers.

VESUVIUS

VESUVIUS

Division A

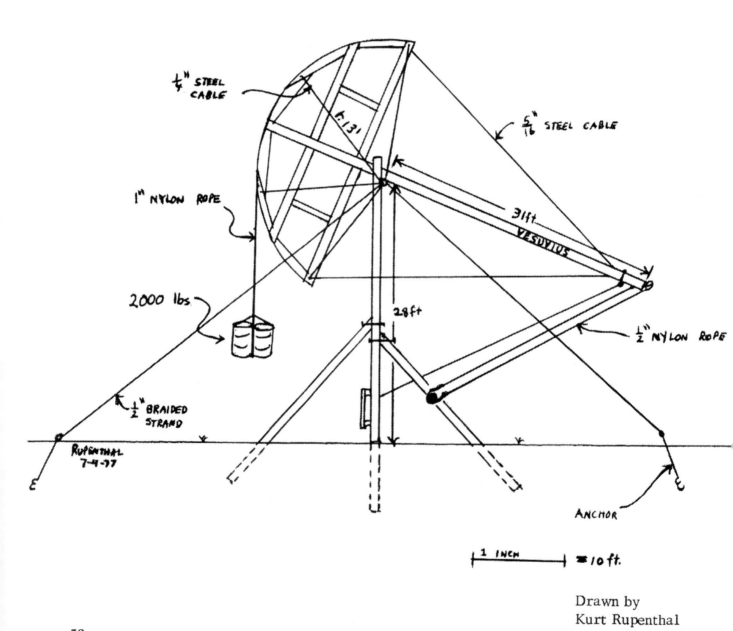

$\frac{1}{4}$" STEEL CABLE

$\frac{5}{16}$" STEEL CABLE

± 13'

31ft

VESUVIUS

1" NYLON ROPE

$\frac{1}{2}$" NYLON ROPE

2000 lbs

28ft

$\frac{1}{2}$" BRAIDED STRAND

Rupenthal 7-4-77

ANCHOR

1 INCH = 10 ft.

Drawn by
Kurt Rupenthal

52

VESUVIUS

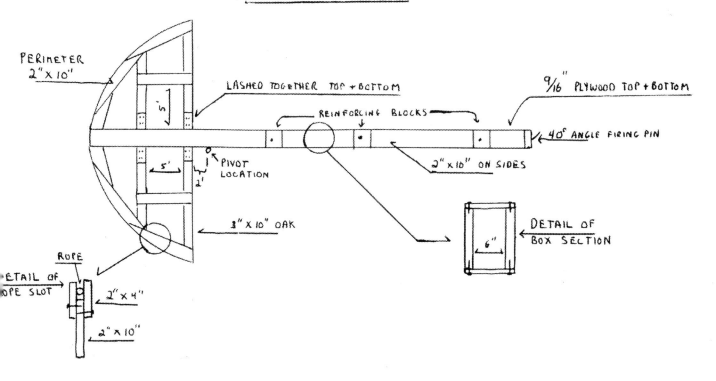

PERIMETER
2" X 10"

LASHED TOGETHER TOP + BOTTOM

REINFORCING BLOCKS

9/16" PLYWOOD TOP + BOTTOM

40° ANGLE FIRING PIN

2" X 10" ON SIDES

PIVOT
LOCATION

3" X 10" OAK

DETAIL OF
BOX SECTION

6"

ROPE

DETAIL OF
ROPE SLOT

2" X 4"

2" X 10"

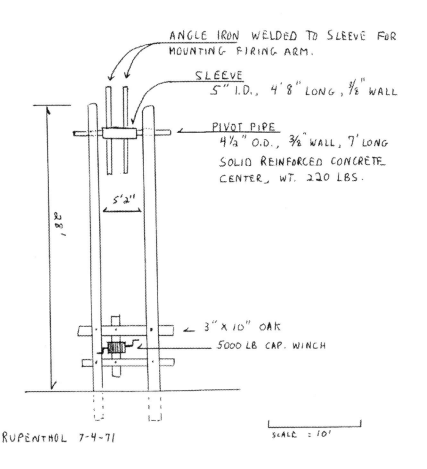

ANGLE IRON WELDED TO SLEEVE FOR
MOUNTING FIRING ARM.

SLEEVE
5" I.D., 4'8" LONG, 3/8" WALL

PIVOT PIPE
4½" O.D., 3/8" WALL, 7' LONG
SOLID REINFORCED CONCRETE
CENTER, WT. 220 LBS.

5'2"

28'

3" X 10" OAK
5000 LB CAP. WINCH

RUPENTHOL 7-4-71

SCALE = 10'

VESUVIUS
SPECIFICATIONS

Total Height	62'
Total Weight	17,000 Lbs.
Firing Arm Length	31'
Sling Length	24'
Winch Capacity	5,000 Lbs.
Counter-weight	2,000 Lbs.
Man Hours Required for Construction	2,500
Actual Cost Excluding Free And Loaned Items	$600
Projected Cost of All Items If Purchased	$4,000

GUIDELINES
FOR
CATAPULT CONSTRUCTION
AND
RECORD SETTING ATTEMPTS

The following guidelines have been devised between 1972 and 1978 by the Consilium Catapultarum and Pompeiiana, Inc., and they have regulated the construction and firing of competitive catapults entered in the National Catapult Contest.

To be officially recognized by Pompeiiana, Inc. any new record-setting attempts must be made in accordance with these guidelines. It should be noted that as of January 1, 1978,

A) attempts at setting new world records in catapulting according to these guidelines may be officially registered with Pompeiiana, Inc. by any individual at least 18 years old,

B) forms to register a catapult record-setting attempt may be requested at least two weeks prior to that attempt at any time during the year,

C) while new records may be set at any time during the year, they will only be publically recognized by Pompeiiana, Inc. during its National Awards Banquet held annually in May, and

D) notarized results of all official catapult record-setting attempts must be returned to Pompeiiana, Inc. on forms which it will provide. Accompanying this return of results to Pompeiiana, Inc. must be frontal, side and rear b/w photographs of the catapult which made the record setting attempts as well as a sketch of the catapult drawn to scale with all dimensions and details included. Also, at least one report of the official catapult shot(s) as reported in the printed media must accompany the results.

I. DEFINITION OF A CATAPULT.

The Romans understood the term "catapulta" to mean an arrow-throwing engine of war, but the modern world generally interprets the term "catapult" to mean any naturally powered ancient device for propelling spears or rocks.

According to this generally accepted definition, all "catapults" recognized by Pompeiiana, Inc. must derive their total power from one of the three natural power sources of A) twisted rope, B) bent wood, or C) the counterweight and be designed to hurl either rocks or spears.

While there is some discussion that the counterweight catapult, or trebuchet, was not fully developed until the middle ages, the principal of leverage on which it operates is so basic to the human experience that Pompeiiana, Inc. believes not only that the Romans were aware of this source of power but that they pioneered the counterweight devices generally credited to medieval engineers.

Catapults represented the most ingenious and intense military efforts of the ancient world, and were undoubtedly larger, more varied and more foreboding than any machines built in the last ten years of modern catapulting. Yet, for the sake of competition, Pompeiiana, Inc. has taken the liberty of distinguishing six separate types of machines, and eight missile weight classes. It has also defined two structural weight classes in which competitive catapults may be constructed.

II. ATTEMPTING TO SET A NEW CATAPULT RECORD.

1. Record-setting catapults may be registered with Pompeiiana, Inc. by any student, adult, or any group of students or adults.
2. Each machine registered must be under the supervision of an adult at least 18 years old.
3. Each catapult registered must be given a classical name.

III. DECIDING THE KIND OF CATAPULT TO BUILD.

1. Perhaps the first decision to be made is whether you would like to build a small catapult that weighs one hundred pounds or under, or a larger machine that weighs over one hundred pounds.

    While heavy-weight rock hurlers can officially fire six different missile classes, and the heavy-weight spear hurlers offer greater challenges, both of the larger catapults require more work and tend to be more expensive to build.

    Light-weight catapults, on the other hand, while easier to design and less expensive to build, are limited to setting records with only a one-pound rock or one-pound spear.

2. Once you have decided on the size of your catapult, you should then decide whether you would like to compete with rocks or spears. The following missile classes have been designated:

CLASS I	10 - 19 lb. rocks
CLASS II	20 - 29 lb. rocks
CLASS III	30 - 39 lb. rocks
CLASS IV	40 - 49 lb. rocks
CLASS V	50 - 74 lb. rocks
CLASS VI	75 - 100 lb. rocks
CLASS VII	one-pound rocks
CLASS VIII	one-pound spears

(A special plaque is awarded for heaviest rock thrown.)

ROCKS -- a) Rocks selected for missile weight classes I - VII may be tooled or mechanically shaped. but they must be natural rock in substance (i.e., no concrete, shotputs metal weights).

b) Leeway has been allowed for rocks entered in missile weight classes I thru VI because of the difficulty in obtaining rocks that weigh exactly the same.

SPEARS -- All spears used for competition by either light-weight or heavy-weight catapults must weigh at least one pound. Students may design their spear as they please, adding fins, a weighted tip, etc. The shaft may be made of wood. metal or a modern synthetic substance. There is no maximum weight limit for spears.

3. Your third decision will be to select the specific Division in which you wish to set a record from the twelve that are listed in Section XI.

IV. INFORMATION ON DESIGNING A CATAPULT.

A catapult's basic design should allow you to harness the source of power you decided to use in Section III. and transfer it to the type of missile you wish to hurl.

For help with the dimensions and details of this basic design you are encouraged to consult the mathematicians and engineers.

You should realize from the beginning that in designing a successful catapult you will be rediscovering knowledge that has been lost in unrecorded history. You will get advice from engineers and mathematicians and gather theories from history books, but most of what you learn will come from your own experimentation with the catapult you build.

Pompeiiana. Inc. suggests the following references:

1. Vitruvius, DE ARCHITECTURA, Vol. II, The Loeb Classical Library (Book X, Chapters X-XVI).
2. THE CROSSBOW, Sir Ralph Payne-Gallway (Random House, New York, N.Y., 1958).

3. GREEK AND ROMAN ARTILLERY HISTORICAL DEVELOPMENT, Marsden (Oxford University Press).
4. GREEK AND ROMAN ARTILLERY TECHNICAL TREATISES, Marsden (Oxford University Press).
5. WEAPONS, A PICTORIAL HISTORY, Edwin Tunis (World Publishing Co., New York, N.Y. 1954).
6. EXPERIMENTAL PHILOSOPHY, J. T. Dezaguliors (1734).
7. CONSTRUCTION AND DECORATIONS OF ARMS AND ARMOR IN ALL COUNTRIES AND ALL TIMES, George Cameron Stone.
8. CATAPULT DESIGN, CONSTRUCTION, AND COMPETITION, Bernard F. Barcio (Pompeiiana, Inc. 1978).

V. CONSTRUCTION GUIDELINES FOR CATAPULTS SETTING NEW RECORDS.

1. General Materials.
   a. All machines must be powered by one of the three Roman power sources (i.e. counterweight, twisted rope, or bent wood) and be designed to fit one of the catapult divisions listed in Sec. XI.
   b. All machines must be designed to be self-supporting in structure.
   c. The supporting structure of each machine must be made of wood.
   d. All machines should be as authentic as possible in structure, material and design; however, for safety, economy and practicality, the following exceptions have been allowed:
      i. The use of steel bolts, nuts and washers.
      ii. The use of steel bands, plate, angle and channel at points of stress.
      iii. The use of steel cable in pulleys and support systems.
      iv. The use of modern winching devices.
      v. The use of modern trigger or release devices.
      vi. The use of rubber tires as part of a bumper system.
      vii. The use of cured and laminated wood.
   e. Although laminated wood may be used, fiberglass and other synthetic materials may not replace wooden firing arms and bent wood power.
   f. Winches used on all machines must test safely beyond the maximum anticipated load.
   g. The projectile hurling device (sling, box, pouch, etc.) must test safely beyond the maximum anticipated load.
   h. All machines must have a safe and tested trigger mechanism, preferably one that allows the machine to be fired from a distance of at least 10 feet.
      i. Pompeiiana, Inc. advises that a trigger mechanism employing a hand-pulled pin not be used on heavy-weight catapults due to past complications.
2. Counterweight Catapults.
   a. For heavy-weight catapults there is a limit of one ton of counterweight which can be added to the weight box after the firing arm is balanced. The weight box may be a steel barrel or other steel construction.
   b. A length limit of 15 feet has been placed on the counterweight end of the firing arm, measuring from the center of the pivot to the end of the counterweight. This counterweight portion of the firing arm may be made from steel components.

c. Steel pipe may be used for the pivot system.

d. At least 51% of the total length of the firing arm, measuring from the firing end from which the missile is projected, must be made of wood.

3. Twisted-rope Catapults.

a. The machine may be powered by hemp, cotton or nylon rope.

b. Steel cable or rope with a rubber or steel core is not allowed for power.

c. At least 51% of the total length of the firing arm, measuring from the firing end from which the missile is projected, must be made of wood.

4. Bent-wood Catapults.

a. The total power source must be bent wood.

b. Spring steel may not be used as a power source.

VI. DECIDING WHERE TO FIRE A CATAPULT.

1. By obtaining proper permission beforehand, your catapult can be fired on school property or on private property suitable for this purpose. In the past, catapultors have even arranged to fire their catapults on U.S. Army reservations and on municipal airport property.

2. In selecting the exact spot on which to situate your machine, spectator and property safety should be your primary concern. Remember, catapults have always been unpredictable in their operation. FOR MAXIMUM SECURITY, PLACE YOUR CATAPULT SO THAT THERE IS A CLEARANCE OF AT LEAST 900 FEET IN FRONT OF AND BEHIND YOUR CATAPULT, AND A CLEARANCE OF AT LEAST 200 FEET ON EACH SIDE OF YOUR CATAPULT. These maximum security clearances are offered for the largest and most powerful machines. The catapult advisor may adjust these clearances depending on the estimated power and range of the catapult to be fired.

VII. DECIDING WHETHER TO FIRE ALONE OR WITH OTHERS.

Each participant can choose to fire his/her catapult(s) alone or to join or host a multi-catapult event.

1. Those wishing to host a multi-catapult event should first make proper arrangements for the use of a site and secure adequate liability insurance coverage.

2. Those wishing to participate in a multi-catapult event and willing to travel with their catapult(s) should make direct arrangements with a known host.

VIII. CHOOSING A RECORD-SETTING DATE.

1. Properly registered firings may be made at any time during the year.

2. Potential problems with weather, construction and test firing should be anticipated before deciding on an official firing date.

3.   If for some reason an officially registered attempt is not completed on the date for which it was registered, a new registration must be submitted two weeks before another official attempt can be made.

IX. OFFICIALLY REGISTERING A RECORD-SETTING ATTEMPT.

1.   To officially register a record-setting attempt with Pompeiiana, Inc., send for a registration form for each record you are attempting to set. Registration forms must be requested at least two weeks prior to any official attempt.

X. FIRING A CATAPULT OFFICIALLY AND REPORTING ITS DISTANCE.

Each record-setting attempt is for the farthest distance in each missile weight class entered. Before firing begins on a field, the crews of all machines present on that field should be agreed as to firing order, procedures for measuring and recording distances, and safety precautions.

1.   A "shot" will be defined as any firing of a machine after the projectile has been loaded. Should a machine misfire during cocking operations, but before the projectile is loaded, this will not be counted as a shot.
2.   Each catapult crew will be allowed to make as many practice shots as it wishes while completing its official shots.
3.   Each catapult is allowed two official shots while attempting to set a new record. To count as an official shot the crew must announce that the shot is official before it is made.
4.   Official distances should be measured and recorded immediately after each shot.
     a)   Shots should be measured from the pivot or source of power on the catapult to the spot where the missile first lands.
     b)   Negative distances (i.e., shots landing on, behind or at the side of a machine) will be recorded as "0" distance.
     c)   For safety and record accuracy, only one machine at a time should fire on a given field, and that machine's distance should be recorded before another machine fires.
5.   Notarized results of the official attempts must be returned to Pompeiiana, Inc. on a form which will be provided. When returning this form, you will be required to attach a) frontal, side, and rear photographs of the catapult entered, b) a sketch of the catapult drawn carefully to scale with all dimensions and details included, and c) at least one report of the achievement as reported in the printed media.

XI. OFFICIAL CATAPULT DIVISIONS.

1. Heavy-weight Catapults (total weight of the catapult is over 100 lbs.).

DIVISION A

Power source: Counterweight
Shoots Class I-VI rocks (cf. Sec. III, 2)

DIVISION B

Power source: Counterweight
Shoots Class VIII spear (cf. Sec. III, 2)

DIVISION C

Power source: Twisted-rope
Shoots Class I-VI rocks (cf. Sec. III, 2)

DIVISION D

Power source: Twisted-rope
Shoots Class VIII spear (cf. Sec. III, 2)

DIVISION E

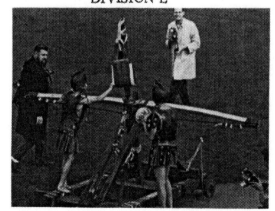

Power source: Bent-wood
Shoots Class I-VI rocks (cf. Sec. III, 2)

DIVISION F

Power source: Bent-wood
Shoots Class VIII spear (cf. Sec. III, 2)

2. Light-weight Catapults (total weight of the catapult is 100 lbs or less).

DIVISION G	DIVISION H

Power source: Counterweight Shoots Class VII rock (cf. Sec. III, 2)	Power source: Counterweight Shoots Class VIII spear (cf. Sec. III, 2)
DIVISION I	DIVISION J

Power source: Twisted-rope Shoots Class VII rock (cf. Sec. III, 2)	Power source: Twisted-rope Shoots Class VIII spear (cf. Sec. III, 2)
DIVISION K	DIVISION L

Power source: Bent-wood Shoots Class VII rock (cf. Sec. III, 2)	Power source: Bent-wood Shoots Class VIII spear (cf. Sec. III, 2)

XII. SAFETY, INSURANCE AND LIABILITY

1. It shall be the responsibility of each participant to anticipate and insure the safety of all crew members. Students working under the guidance of an adult advisor will have to be properly instructed in the safe use of tools and on special safety measures pertinent to each machine.

2. Pompeiiana, Inc. recommends that all crew members of rock-hurling machines wear safety head gear for all practice and competitive shots.

3. Safety guidelines should be established on each competition field to keep crew members and spectators a safe distance from machines during all practice and competitive firing. REMEMBER THAT CATAPULTS HAVE BEEN KNOWN TO FIRE BACKWARDS AS WELL AS FORWARDS.

4. Before undertaking to build and fire a catapult, each participant or group should be sure they have sufficient accident and liability insurance coverage.

5. POMPEIIANA, INC. CAN ACCEPT NO LIABILITY FOR INJURIES OR DAMAGES SUSTAINED IN CONNECTION WITH ANY ATTEMPT TO BREAK THE CATAPULTING RECORDS MAINTAINED BY POMPEIIANA, INC.

6. It is advisable that, prior to their beginning work on the project, all participants under the age of 18 submit signed parent permission slips to their adult advisor.

XIII. AWARDS

1. Ribbons:
    a) Participation ribbons will be awarded to each individual or group that registers an official attempt to set a new catapulting record and actually completes that attempt (regardless of the success of setting a new record.)

2. Plaques:
    a) Plaques will be awarded in the name of the catapult for each new record successfully set and reported according to the instructions in Sections IX and X.

3. All awards will be presented annually at a National Awards Banquet to be held in mid-May in Indianapolis, Indiana. Awards will be mailed to those unable to attend this banquet.

Catapult Album

WHILE PHOTOGRAPHS OF ALL 112 CATAPULTS
ENTERED IN THE NATIONAL CATAPULT
CONTEST ARE NOT INCLUDED IN THIS ALBUM,
EVERY CATAPULT FOR WHICH PHOTOGRAPHS
WERE AVAILABLE TO POMPEIIANA, INC. HAS
BEEN INCLUDED SO THAT A VISUAL RECORD
OF AS MANY MACHINES AS POSSIBLE WOULD
BE PRESERVED FOR THOSE INTERESTED IN
THEIR CONSTRUCTION.

THE CATAPULT PHOTOGRAPHS ARE ARRANGED
ALPHABETICALLY WITH BUILDER INFORMATION
HAVING BEEN RECORDED IN THOSE SECTIONS OF
THIS BOOK ENTITLED "WORLD RECORDS IN
CATAPULTING AND THE CATAPULTS THAT HAVE
SET THEM," AND "BEST DISTANCES OF OTHER
CATAPULTS FIRED IN THE NATIONAL CATAPULT
CONTEST 1972-1977."

PROJECTILE AND RANGE: 10 lb rock 110'

ARES II

PROJECTILES AND RANGE: 10 lb rock 583', 20 lb rock 444', 30 lb rock 366'6"
40 lb rock 240', 50 lb rock 282', 75 lb rock 188'10"

Photos courtesy of Mr. and Mrs. Carl Dortch

PROJECTILE AND RANGE: 1 lb spear 18'

PROJECTILE AND RANGE: 1 lb rock 67'

PROJECTILE AND RANGE: 10 lb rock 139'

PROJECTILE AND RANGE: 1 lb spear 438'3" (World Record)

PROJECTILE AND RANGE: 1 lb rock 239' (World Record)

PROJECTILE AND RANGE: 1,400 lb boulder 8' (World Record)

PROJECTILES AND RANGE: 10 lb rock 237'7", 30 lb rock 132'3", 40 lb rock 101'
50 lb rock 53'3", 75 lb rock 38'5"

PROJECTILE AND RANGE: 1 lb spear 110'

Photo above by Bob Hubbard

PROJECTILES AND RANGE: 10 lb rock 371', 20 lb rock 299', 30 lb rock 207'7"
40 lb rock 137', 50 lb rock 76'

PROJECTILES AND RANGE: 10 lb rock 119'2", 20 lb rock 82'9"
30 lb rock 62', 75 lb rock 13'

Photo above by Mary Sue Best

PROJECTILES AND RANGE: 10 lb rock 45'3", 20 lb rock 33', 30 lb rock 40'3"

PROJECTILE AND RANGE: 1 lb rock 191'6" (World Record)

PROJECTILE AND RANGE: 1 lb rock 186'3" (World Record)

PROJECTILE AND RANGE: 1 lb rock 137'8"

PROJECTILE AND RANGE: 1 lb rock 60'6"

PROJECTILE AND RANGE: 1 lb spear 577'

PROJECTILE AND RANGE: 1 lb rock 144'8"

PROJECTILES AND RANGE: 10 lb rock 36'9", 20 lb rock 18'2", 40 lb rock 9'1"

OTUS & EPHIALTUS

PROJECTILES AND RANGE: 75 lb rock 52', 335 lb rock 43'

85

PROJECTILES AND RANGE: 10 lb rock 310'10", 20 lb rock 231'6", 30 lb rock 195'
40 lb rock 208'9", 50 lb rock 165', 75 lb rock 115'7"

PROJECTILE AND RANGE: 1 lb rock 24'6"

PROJECTILE AND RANGE: 1 lb spear 294'2"

PROJECTILE AND RANGE: 1 lb rock 168'

PROJECTILES AND RANGE: 10 lb rock 541'3", 20 lb rock 537', 30 lb rock 453'
40 lb rock 418', 50 lb rock 403', 75 lb rock 237'4"

PROJECTILE AND RANGE: 1 lb spear 167'

PROJECTILE AND RANGE: 10 lb rock 50'5"

PROJECTILE AND RANGE: 1 lb rock 181'10"

PROJECTILES AND RANGE: 10 lb rock 98', 20 lb rock 38', 30 lb rock 39'
40 lb rock 36', 50 lb rock 30', 75 lb rock 15'

PROJECTILES AND RANGE: 40 lb rock 175', 50 lb rock 226', 75 lb rock 174'8"

PROJECTILE AND RANGE: 75 lb rock 176'1"

STIRPS
MALORUM
EDINA LATIN CLUBS

TORQUEATOR

PROJECTILE AND RANGE: 1 lb spear 179'8"

PROJECTILES AND RANGE: 10 lb rock 32'6", 20 lb rock 7'2"

MEDIA COVERAGE OF CATAPULTING

AND

AUDIO-VISUAL RECORDINGS

From its beginning in 1965, catapulting has attracted the attention of national media in one form or another. The NBC news team of Huntley-Brinkley covered the firing of the Mars I in 1966. Coverage was given to catapulting on the NBC "First Tuesday" programs in 1969 and 1970, and on the NBC "Chronolog" programs in 1971 and 1972.

The winners of the First and Fifth National Catapult Contests, David Dortch and Mary Hyde, appeared in special segments of ABC's "To Tell the Truth."

On May 18, 1976, the New York Times (p.31) ran a syndicated article on The National Catapult Contest which was picked up by major newspapers across the country.

After publishing a brief article on catapulting in the April 6, 1970, issue, Sports Illustrated came back to cover The National Catapult Contest thoroughly in an article entitled "First Among Those Who Cast Stones" by writer Bruce Newman. The article appeared in the June 7, 1976, issue of Sports Illustrated, pp. 64 & 66.

The magazine Seventeen ran an article on the new interest in catapulting in its May, 1975, issue. Articles also appeared in the Classical Outlook (February, 1974), and in the Brittanica Review of Foreign Language Education (1971 issue, pp. 201-2).

CONCLUSION

Not everyone who takes an interest in catapults will eventually
attempt to rebuild one of these ancient machines, much less
strive to set modern catapulting records. It takes an individual
who is both driven by a unique determination and able to withstand
the pessimism of those not similarly inclined.

As Louis Vaczek, an occasional writer for the Saturday Evening
Post once wrote in an unpublished manuscript, "What was the
usefulness of a catapult today, if it ever did get built? The
answer: no earthly use whatever. Those who cannot understand
why this would fire up a group of young people really do not
understand young people. It is not that they want to do something
useless. Far from it. It has to do with the simple fact that the
project would test their ingenuity to the utmost and would belong
exclusively to them. That the object they were to make had no
relevance to modern life was of no consequence."

Perhaps it is true that only strangely inspired people would take
on such a project. Unfashionable though their interest may be,
those who involve themselves with a catapult invariably find
within themselves the enthusiasm, lit by a private spark of
wonder, to participate meaningfully in the work. Almost at once
and without planning, the task draws participants into a mature
collaboration many have never known before. Here is a project
that teaches one how to learn--not to parrot, but to generate
knowledge. Catapultors discover that they are collecting real
information concerning a phenomenon about which very few
people in the world know anything. An experienced catapultor
becomes one of the world's few living experts on workable
catapult design and construction.

While this interest in modern catapulting was born as a class
project of a group of secondary school students studying Julius
Caesar's Gallic Wars, it has spread an enthusiasm and interest
nation-wide, and has established goals and records which now
serve as challenges to all--adults and students alike--who
share a deep-seated interest in the ancient art of catapulting.

DE CATAPULTIS SEMPER DUBITANDUM EST!

Section Three

The
Projectile Throwing Engines
of the Ancients

Sir Ralph Payne-Gallwey

A SUMMARY OF

THE HISTORY, CONSTRUCTION AND EFFECTS IN WARFARE

OF THE

PROJECTILE – THROWING ENGINES

OF THE ANCIENTS

BY

SIR RALPH PAYNE-GALLWEY, B^{T.}

1907

THE PROJECTILE-THROWING ENGINES OF
THE ANCIENTS

CONTENTS

PREFACE

SINCE my recent book on mediæval archery and ancient weapons was issued,[1] I have obtained a considerable amount of information concerning the projectile engines of the Greeks and Romans. I now print a concise account of the history, construction, and effects in warfare of these engines.

In this summary the additional notes I have acquired are included.

R. P. G.

THIRKLEBY PARK,
   THIRSK :
      Dec. 1906

---

[1] *The Crossbow, mediæval and Modern, Military and Sporting : Its Construction, History, and Management. With a Treatise on the Balista and Catapult of the Ancients.* 220 illustrations. Messrs. Longmans & Co., 39 Paternoster Row, London.

PART I

INTRODUCTORY NOTES ON ANCIENT PROJECTILE ENGINES

Of ancient Greek authors who have left us accounts of these engines, Heron (284-221 B.C.) and Philo (about 200 B.C.) are the most trustworthy.

Both these mechanicians give plans and dimensions with an accuracy that enables us to reconstruct the machines, if not with exactitude at any rate with sufficient correctness for practical application.

Though in the books of Athenaeus, Biton, Apollodorus, Diodorus, Procopius, Polybius and Josephus we find incomplete descriptions, these authors, especially Josephus, frequently allude to the effects of the engines in warfare ; and scanty as is the knowledge they impart, it is useful and explanatory when read in conjunction with the writings of Heron and Philo.

Among the Roman historians and military engineers, Vitruvius and Ammianus are the best authorities.

Vitruvius copied his descriptions from the Greek writers, which shows us that the Romans adopted the engines from the Greeks.

Of all the old authors who have described the engines, we have but copies of the original writings. It is therefore natural that we should come across many phrases and drawings which are evidently incorrect, as a result of repeated transcription, and which we know to be at fault though we cannot actually prove them to be so.

With few exceptions, all the authors named simply present us with their own ideas when they are in doubt respecting the mechanical details and performances of the engines they wish to describe.

All such spurious information is, of course, more detrimental than helpful to our elucidation of their construction and capabilities.

It frequently happens that in a mediæval picture of one of these machines some important mechanical detail is omitted, or, from the difficulty of portraying it correctly, is purposely concealed by figures of soldiers, an omission that may be supplied by reference to other representations of the same weapon.

Fig 1. — Besieging a Fortified Town With a Battery of Catapults and Balistas.
Criticism. — In this picture the balistas are fairly correct, but the catapults are too small.
From Polybius.   Edition 1727

It is, indeed, impossible to find a complete working plan of any one of these old weapons, a perfect design being only obtainable by consulting many ancient authorities, and, it may be said, piecing together the details of construction they individually give.

We have no direct evidence as to when the engines for throwing projectiles were invented.

It does not appear that King Shalmaneser II. of Assyria (859-825 B.C.) had any, for none are depicted on the bonze doors of the palace of Balâwat, now in the British Museum, on which his campaigns are represented, though his other weapons of attack and defence are clearly shown.

The earliest allusion is the one in the Bible, where we read of Uzziah, who reigned from B.C. 808-9 to B.C. 756-7. 'Uzziah made in Jerusalem engines invented by cunning men, to be on the towers and upon the bulwarks, to shoot arrows and great stones withal." (2 Chronicles xxvi. 15.)

Diodorus tells us that the engines were first seen about 400 B.C., and that when Dionysisu of Syracuse organized his great expedition against the Carthaginians (397 B.C.) there was a genius among the experts collected from all over the world, and that this man designed the engines that cast stones and javelins.

From the reign of Dionysius and for many subsequent centuries, or till near the close of the fourteenth, projectile-throwing engines are constantly mentioned by military historians.

But it was not till the reign of Philip of Macedon (360-336 B.C.) and that of his son Alexander the Great (336-323 B.C.) that their improvement was carefully attended to and their value in warfare fully recognised.

As before stated, the Romans adopted the engines from the Greeks.

Vitruvius and other historians tell us this, and even copy their descriptions of them from the Greek authors, though too often with palpable inaccuracy.

To ascertain the power and mechanism of these ancient engines a very close study of all the old authors who wrote about them is essential, with a view to extracting here and there useful facts amid what are generally verbose and confused references.

There is no doubt that the engines made and used by the Romans after their conquest of Greece (B.C. 146), in the course of two or three centuries became inferior to the original machines previously constructed by the Greek artificers.

There efficiency chiefly suffered because the art of manufacturing their important parts was gradually neglected and allowed to become lost.

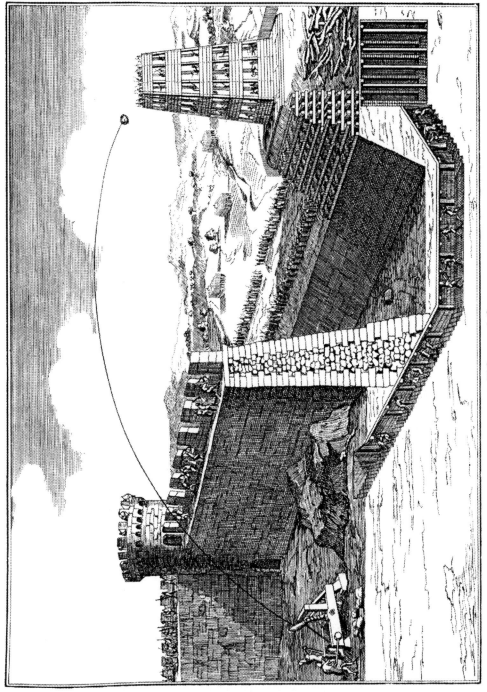

FIG. 2. – A SIEGE.

Criticism. – The picture is open to the spectator in order that he may see both defenders and besiegers at work. The besieged have just cast a stone from a catapult. The stone is falling on the movable tower belonging to the attacking side.

From Polybius. Edition 1727.

For instance, how to make the skein of sinew that bestowed the very life and existence on every projectile-casting engine of the ancients.

The tendons of which the sinew was composed, the animals from which it was taken, and the manner in which it was prepared, we can never learn now.

Every kind of sinew, or hair or ropes, with which I have experimented, either breaks or loses its elasticity in a comparatively short time, if great pressure is applied. It has then to be renewed at no small outlay of expense and trouble. Rope skeins, with which we are obliged to fit our models, cannot possibly equal in strength and above all in elasticity, skeins of animal sinew or even of hair.

The formation of the arm or arms of an engine, whether it is a catapult with its single upright arm or a balista with its pair of lateral ones is another difficulty which cannot now be overcome, for we have no idea how these arms were made to sustain the great strain they had to endure.

We know that the arm of a large engine was composed of several spars of wood and lengths of thick sinew fitted longitudinally, and then bound round with broad strips of raw hide which would afterwards set nearly as hard and tight as a sheath of metal.

We know this, but we do not know the secret of making a light and flexible arm of sufficient strength to bear such a strain as was formerly applied to it in a catapult or a balista.

Certainly, by shaping an arm of great thickness we can produce one that will not fracture, but substance implies weight, and undue weight prevents the arm from acting with the speed requisite to cast its projectile with good effect.

A heavy and ponderous arm of solid wood cannot, of course, rival in lightness and effectiveness a composite one of wood, sinew and hide.

The former is necessarily inert and slow in its action of slinging a stone, while the latter would, in comparison, be as quick and lively as a steel spring.

When the art of producing the perfected machines of the Greeks was lost, they were replaced by less effective contrivances.

If the knowledge of constructing the great catapult of the ancients in its original perfection had been retained, such a clumsy engine as the mediæval trebuchet would never have gained popularity. The trebuchet derived its power from the gravity of an immense weight at one end of its pivoted arm tipping up the other end, to which a sling was attached for throwing a stone.

As regards range, there could be no comparison between the efficiency of a trebuchet, however large, as worked merely by a counterpoise, and that of an engine deriving its power from the elasticity of an immense coil of tightly twisted sinew.

It is certain that if the latter kind of engine had survived in its perfect state the introduction of cannon would have been considerably delayed, for the effects in warfare of the early cannon were for a long period decidedly inferior to those of the best projectile engines of the ancients.

Notwithstanding many difficulties, I have succeeded in reconstructing, though of course on a considerably smaller scale, the chief projectile throwing engines of the ancients, and with a success that enables them to compare favourably, as regards their range, with the Greek and Roman weapons, they represent.

Still, my engines are by no means perfect in their mechanism, and are, besides, always liable to give way under the strain of working.

One reason of this is that all modern engines of the kind require to be worked to their utmost capacity, *i.e.* to the verge of their breaking point, to obtain from them results that at all equal those of their prototypes.

A marked difference between the ancient engines and their modern imitations, however excellent the latter may be, is, that the former did their work easily, and well within their strength, and thus without any excessive strain which might cause their collapse after a short length of service. [1]

The oft-disputed question as to the distance to which catapults and balistas shot their projectiles can be solved with approximate accuracy by comparing their performances--as given by ancient military writers--with the results obtainable from modern reproductions.

While treating of this matter we should carefully consider the position and surroundings of the engines when engaged in a siege, and especially the work for which they were designed.

As an example, archers, with the advantage of being stationed on high towers and battlements, would be well able to shoot arrows from 270 to 280 yards. For this reason it was necessary for the safe manipulation of the attacking engines that they should be placed at about 300 yards from the outer walls of any fortress they were assailing.

As a catapult or a balista was required not only to cast its missile among the soldiers on the ramparts of a fortified place, but also to send it clear over the walls amid the houses and people within the defences, it is evident that the

[1] Again, though my largest catapult will throw a stone to a great distance it cannot throw one of nearly the weight it should be able to do, considering the size of its frame, skein of cord and mechanism. In this respect it is decidedly inferior to the ancient engine.

engines must have had a range of from 400 to 500 yards, or more, to be as serviceable and destructive as they undoubtedly were.

Josephus tells us that at the siege of Jerusalem, A.D. 70 ('Wars of the Jews,' Book V. Chapter VI.), stones weighing a talent (57 ¾ lbs. avoirdupois) were thrown by the catapults to a distance of two or more 'stades.'

This statement may be taken as trustworthy, for Josephus relates what he personally witnessed and his comments are those of a commander of high rank and intelligence.

Two or more 'stades,' or let us say 2 to 2 ¼ 'stades,' represent 400 to 450 yards. Remarkable and conclusive testimony confirming the truth of what

FIG. 3.--A FORTIFIED TOWN BEING BOMBARDED BY A CATAPULT.

Criticism.-The stones thrown by the besieged may be seen falling in the trenches of the besiegers. The catapult depicted is drawn on much too small a scale.

From Polybius. Edition 1727.

we read in Josephus is the face that my largest catapult--though doubtless much smaller and less powerful than those referred to by the historian--throws a stone ball of 8 lbs. in weight to a range of from 450 to nearly 500 yards.

It is easy to realise that the ancients, with their great and perfect engines fitted with skeins of sinew, could cast a far heavier stone than one of 8 lbs., and to a longer distance than 500 yards.

Agesistratus,[1] a Greek writer who flourished B.C. 200, and who wrote a treatise on making arms for war, estimated that some of the engines shot from 3 ½ to 4 'stades' (700 to 800 yards).

Though such a very long flight as this appears almost incredible, I can adduce no sound reason for doubting its possibility. From recent experiments I am confident I could now build an engine of a size and power to accomplish such a feat if light missiles were used, and if its cost were not a consideration.

FIG. 4.-A SIEGE CATAPULT (WITHOUT A SLING).
From Polybius. Edition 1727.

[1] The writings of Agesistratus are non-extant but are quoted by Athenæus.

PART II

THE CATAPULT (WITH A SLING)

Fig. 5.-A Siege Catapult (Without A Sling).

Criticism.-This engine was moved into position on rollers and then props were placed under its sides to adjust the range of the projectile.

The end of the arm was secured by the notch of the large iron catch and was released by striking down the handle of the catch with a heavy mallet.

The arm is, however, too long for the height of the crossbar against which it strikes and would probably break off at its centre.

The hollow for the stone is much too large, as a stone big enough to fit it could not be cast by a weapon of the dimensions shown in the picture.

From an Illustrated Manuscript, Fifteenth Century (no. 7239), Bibl.Nat.Paris.

The mediæval catapult was usually fitted with an arm that had a hollow or cup at its upper end in which was placed the stone it projected, as shown above in fig. 5.[1] I find, however, that the original and more perfect form of this engine, as employed by the Greeks and ancient Romans, had a sling, made of rope and leather, attached to its arm.[2] (Fig.6, following page.)

[1] See also *The Crossbow, etc.,* Chapters LV., LVI., illustrations 193 to 202.

[2] In mediæval times catapults which had not slings cast great stones, but only to a short distance in comparison with the earlier weapons of the same kind that were equipped with slings. I can find no

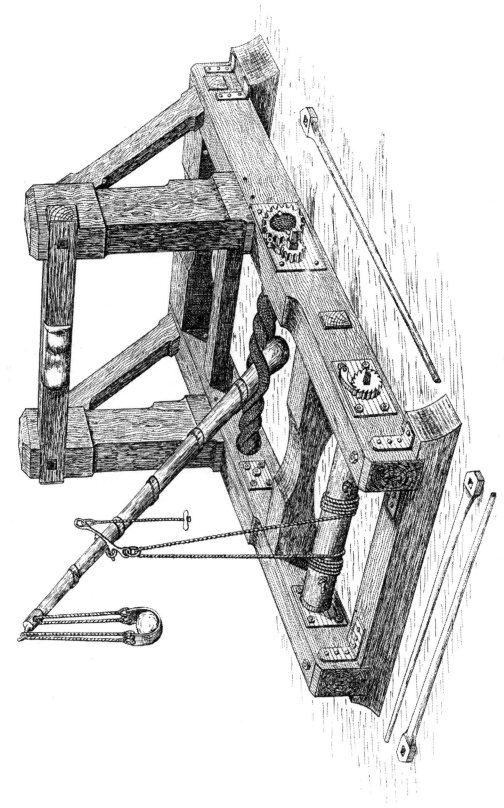

FIG 6. -- SKETCH PLAN OF A CATAPULT FOR SLINGING STONES ITS ARM BEING PARTLY WOUND DOWN.
Approximate scale : ½ in. = 1 ft.

The addition of a sling to the arm of a catapult increases its power by at least a third. For example, the catapult described in Chapters LV,. LVI., of my book,[1] will throw a round stone 8 lbs. in weight, from 350 to 360 yards, but the same engine with the advantage of a sling to its arm will cast the 8-lb. Stone from 450 to 460 yards, and when its skein is twisted to its limit of tension to nearly 500 yards.

If the upper end of the arm if a catapult is shaped into a cup to receive the stone, as shown in fig. 5, p. 11, the arm is, of necessity, large and heavy at this part.

If, on the other hand, the arm is equipped with a sling, as shown in fig. 6, opposite page, it can be tapered from its butt-end upwards, and is then much lighter and recoils with far more speed than an arm that has an enlarged extremity for holding its missile.

When the arm is fitted with a sling, it is practically lengthened by as much as the length of the sling attached to it, and this, too, without any appreciable increase in its weight.

The longer the arm of a catapult, the longer is its sweep through the air, and thus the farther will it cast its projectile, provided it is not of undue weight.

The difference in this respect is as between the range of a short sling and that of a long one, when both are used by a school-boy for slinging pebbles.

This increase of power conferred by the addition of a sling to the arm of a catapult is surprising.

A small model I constructed for throwing a stone ball, one pound in weight, will attain a distance of 200 yards when used with an arm that has a cup for holding the ball, though when a sling is fitted to the arm the range of the engine is at once increased to 300 yards.

The only historian who distinctly tells us that the catapult of the Greeks and Romans had a sling to its arm, is Ammianus Marcellinus. This author flourished about 380 AD., and a closer study of his writings, and those of his contemporaries, led me to carry out experiments with catapults and balistas which I had not contemplated when my work dealing with the projectile engines of the Ancients was published.

allusions or pictures to show that during this period any engine was used with a sling except the trebuchet, a post-Roman invention. All evidence goes to prove that the secret of making the skein and other important parts of a catapult was in a great measure lost within a couple of centuries after the Romans copied the weapon from their conquered enemies the Greeks, with the result that the trebuchet was introduced for throwing stones.

The catapult was gradually superceded as the art of its construction was neglected, and its efficiency in sieges was therefrom decreased.

The catapults of the fifth and sixth centuries were very inferior to those described by Josephus as being used at the sieges of Jerusalem and Jotopata (A.D. 70, A.D. 67), p. 37.

[1] *The Crossbow, etc.*

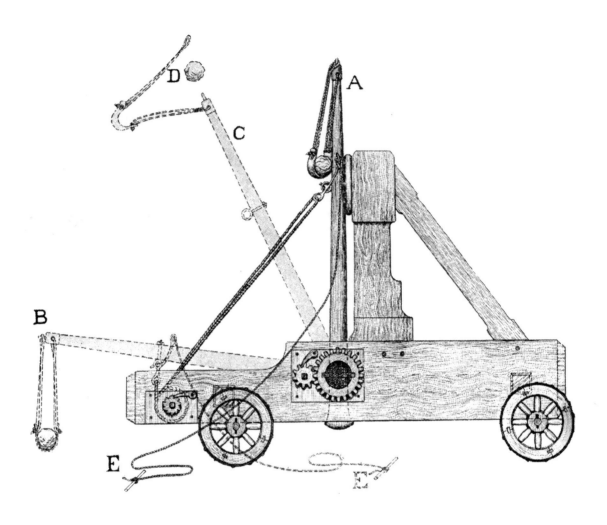

FIG 7. – CATAPULT (WITH A SLING). Side view of frame and mechanism.
Scale : ½ in. = 1 ft.

Ammianus writes of the catapult[1]:

'In the middle of the ropes[2] rises a wooden arm like a chariot pole . . . to the top of the arm hangs a sling . . . when the battle is commenced a round stone is set in the sling . . . four soldiers on each side of the engine wind the arm down till it is almost level with the ground . . . when the arm is set free it springs up and hurls forth from its sling the stone, which is certain to crush whatever it strikes. This engine was formerly called the "scorpion," because it has it sting erect,[3] but later ages have given it the name of Onager, or wild ass, for when wild asses are chased they kick the stones behind them.'

FIG. 7. — CATAPULT (WITH A SLING), SEE OPPOSITE PAGE.

A.   The arm at rest, ready to be wound down by the rope attached to it and also to the wooden roller of the windlass. The stone may be seen in the sling.

The upper end of the pulley rope is hitched by a metal slip-hook (fig.6, p. 12) to a ring-bolt secured to the arm just below the sling.

B.   The position of the arm when fully wound down by means of the windlass and rope. See also EE, fig. 8, page 16.

C.   The position of the arm at the moment the stone D leaves the sling, which it does at an angle of about 45 degrees.

E.   By pulling the cord E the arm B is at once released from the slip-hook and, taking an upward sweep of 90 degrees, returns to its original position at A.

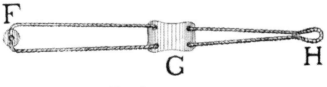

THE SLING (OPEN)

[F.   Its fixed end which passes through a hole near the top of the arm.

G.   The leather pocket for the stone.

H.   The loop which is hitched over the iron pin at the top of the arm when the stone is in position in the sling, as shown at A and B, fig. 7.]

[1]   *Roman History*, Book XXIII., Chapter IV.
[2]   *i.e.* in the middle of the twisted skein formed of ropes of sinew or hair.
[3]   The upright and tapering arm of a catapult, with the iron pin on its top for the loop of the sling, is here fancifully likened to the erected tail of an angry scorpion with its sting protruding.

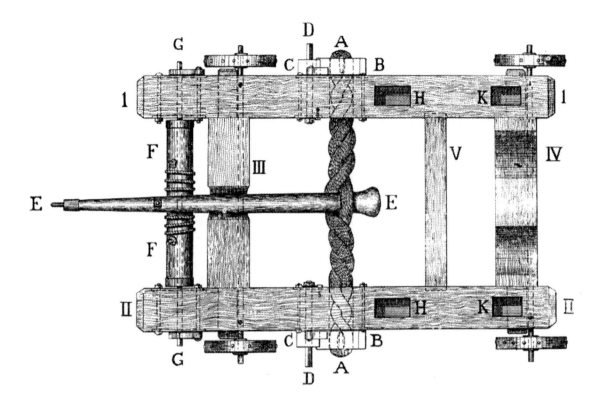

FIG. 8.-- CATAPULT (WITH A SLING). Surface view of frame and mechanism. Scale : ½ in. = 1 foot.
The arm EE is here shown wound down to its full extent. (Compare with B, fig. 7, page 14.)

I.   I.   } The side pieces
II.   II.

III.   IV.   The large cross-pieces
        V.   The small cross-pieces

The ends of the cross-piece beams are stepped into the side pieces.

AA.   The skein of twisted cord.

BB.   The large winding wheels. The skein is stretched between these wheels, its ends passing through the sides of the frame, and then through the wheels and over their cross-bars. (Fig. 12, p.19.)

By turning with a long spanner (fig. 6, p. 12) the squared ends of the spindles DD, the pinion wheels CC rotate the large wheels BB and cause the latter to twist the skein AA, between the halves of which the arm EE is placed.

FF.   The wooden roller which winds down the arm EE. (Fig. 6, p. 12.)

The roller is revolved by four men (two on each side of the engine) who fit long spanners on the squared ends of the iron spindle GG.

This spindle passes through the centre of the roller and through the sides of the frame.

The small cogged wheels, with their checks, which are fitted to the ends of the spindle GG, prevent the roller from reversing as the arm is being wound down. (Fig. 6, p. 12.)

HH. The hollows in the sides of the frame which receive the lower tenons of the two uprights. Between the tops of these uprights the cross-beam is fixed against which the arm of the catapult strikes when it is released. (Fig. 6, p. 12.)

KK. The hollows for the lower tenons of the two sloping supports which prevent the uprights, and the cross-beam between them, from giving way when the arm recoils. (Fig. 6, p. 12.)

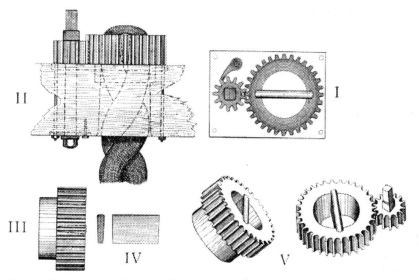

FIG. 9.—ONE OF THE PAIR OF WINCHES OF A CATAPULT. Scale : $^1/_{16}$ in. = 1 in.

I. Surface view of one of the winches and of the thick iron plate in which the socket of the large winding wheel of the winch revolves.

II. View of a winch (from above) as fitted into one of the sides of the frame of the catapult. One end of the twisted skein may be seen turned round the cross-bar of the large wheel.

III. Side view of the large wheel of a winch.

IV. The cross-bar of one of the large wheels. These pieces fit like wedges into tapering slots cut down the barrels, or inside surfaces, of their respective wheels.

V. Perspective view of the wheels of a winch.

The winches are the vital parts of the catapult as they generate its projectile power.

They are employed to twist tightly the skein of cord between which the butt-end of the arm of the engine is placed.

The cord composing the skein is stretched to and fro across and through the sides of the catapult, and alternately through the insides of the large wheels and over their cross-bars ; as show in fig. 8, p. 16.

FIG. 10.

FIG. 10. THE IRON SLIP HOOK

This simple contrivance not only pulled down the arm of a catapult but was also the means of setting it free. However great the strain on the slip-hook, it will, if properly shaped, easily effect the release of the arm.

The trajectory of the missile can be regulated by this form of release, as the longer the distance the arm is pulled down the higher the angle at which the projectile is thrown.

On the other hand, the shorter the distance the arm is drawn back, the lower the trajectory of its missile.

The slip-hook will release the arm of the engine at any moment, whether it is fully or only partially wound down by the windlass.

The slip-hook of the large catapult shown in fig. 6, p. 12 , has a handle, *i.e.* lever, 10 inches long, the point of the hook, which passes through the eye-bolt secured to the arm, being one inch in diameter.

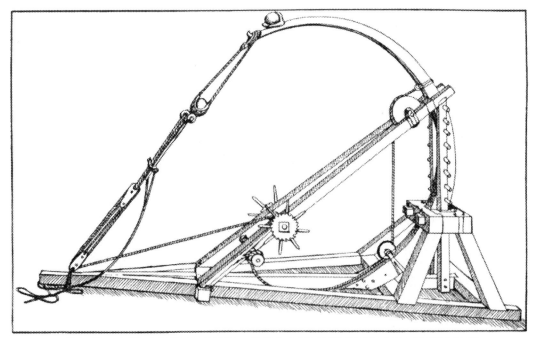

FIG. II. – A Spring Engine with a Sling Attached to its Arm, which cast
Two Stones at the Same Time.

From ' Il Codice Atlantico, ' Leonardo da Vinci. 1445-1520.

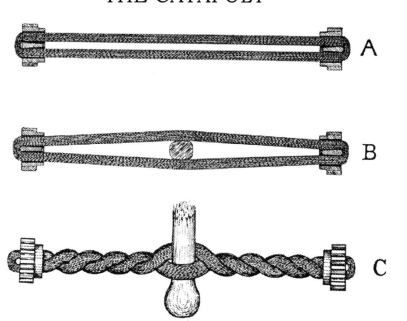

Fig. 12.-- THE SKEIN OF CORD

A.	The skein as first wound over the cross-bars of the large wheels (shown in section) of the winches.

B.	The skein with the butt-end of the arm (shown in section) placed between its halves.

C.	The skein as it appears when tightly twisted up by the winches. Compare with AA, fig. 8, p. 16.

Cord of Italian hemp, about ¼ in. thick, is excellent for small catapults. For large ones, horsehair rope, ½ in. thick, is the best and most elastic. Whatever is used, the material of the skein must be thoroughly soaked in neats-foot oil for some days previously, or it is sure to fray and cut under the friction of being very tightly twisted. Oil will also preserve the skein from damp and decay for many years.

HOW TO WORK THE CATAPULT

There is little to write under this heading ; as the plans, details of construction and illustrations will, I trust, elucidate its management.

The skein should never remain in a tightly twisted condition, but should be untwisted when the engine is not in use.

Previous to using the catapult its winches should be turned with the long spanner, fig. 6, p. 12, first the winch on one side of the engine and then the one on the other side of it, and each to exactly the same amount.

Small numerals painted on the surfaces of the large wheels near their edges, will show how much they have been revolved ; in this way their rotation can be easily arranged to correspond.

As the skein of cord is being twisted by the very powerful winches, the arm will gradually press with increasing force against the cross-beam between the uprights. The arm should be so tightly pressed against the fender, or cushion of straw, attached to the centre of this beam, that, whether large or small, it cannot be pulled back the least distance by hand.

If the skein of my largest catapult is fully tightened up by the winches, three strong men are unable to draw the arm back with a rope even an inch from the cross-beam, though the windlass has to pull it down from six to seven feet when the engine is made ready for action.

When the skein is as tight as it should be, attach the slip-hook to the ring-bolt in the arm and place the stone in the sling suspended from the top of the arm.

The arm can now be drawn down by means of long spanners fitted to the windlass. Directly the arm is as low as it should be, or as is desired, it should be instantly released by pulling the cord fastened to the lever of the slip-hook.

The least delay in doing this, and the resulting continuation of the immense strain on the arm, may cause it to fracture when it would not otherwise have done so.

The plans I have given are those of my largest engine, which, ponderous as it seems—(it weighs two tons)—is, however, less than half the size of the catapult used by the ancients for throwing stones of from forty to fifty pounds in weight.

As the plans are accurately drawn to scale, the engine can easily be reproduced in a smaller size.

An interesting model can be constructed that has an arm 3 feet in length, and a skein of cord about 4 inches in diameter. It can be worked by one man and will throw a stone, the size of an orange, to a range of 300 yards.

The sling, when suspended with the stone in position, should be one third the length of the arm, as shown in fig. 7, p. 14.

If the sling is shortened, the ball will be thrown at a high elevation. If the sling is lengthened, the ball will travel at a lower angle and with much more velocity.

PART III

THE BALISTA

FIG. 13.— BALISTA FOR DISCHARGING HEAVY ARROWS OR JAVELINS.
Approximate scale : ½ in. = 1 foot.

THIS engine is here shown ready for discharge with its bow-string drawn to its full extent by the windlass.

The heavy iron-tipped arrow rests in the shallow wooden trough or groove which travels along the stock.

The trough has a strip of wood, in the form of a keel, fixed beneath it. This keel travels to or fro in a dove-tailed slot cut along the upper surface of the stock for the greater part of its length. (F, fig. 14, p.23.)

The arrow is laid in the trough before the bow-string is stretched. (A, B, fig. 14, p. 23.)

The balista is made ready for use by turning the windlass. The windlass pulls back the sliding trough, and the arrow resting in it, along the stock of the engine, till the bow-string is at its proper tension for discharging the projectile. (Fig.13, p. 21)

As the trough and the arrow are drawn back together, the arrow can be safely laid in position before the engine is prepared for action.

The catch for holding the bow-string, and the trigger for releasing it, are fixed to the solid after-end of the wooden trough. (Fig. 14, p.23.)

The two ratchets at the sides of the after-end of the trough travel over and engage, as they pass along, the metal cogs fixed on either side of the stock. (Fig.14, p. 23.)[1]

By this arrangement the trough can be securely retained, in transit, at any point between the one it started from and the one it attains when drawn back to its full extent by the windlass.

As the lock and trigger of the balista are fixed to the after-end of the sliding trough (fig. 14, p. 23), it will be realised that the arrow could be discharged at any moment required in warfare, whether the bow-string was fully or only partially stretched.

In this respect the balista differed from the crossbow, which it somewhat resembled, as in a crossbow the bow-string cannot be set free by the trigger at an intermediate point, but only when it is drawn to the lock of the weapon.

It will be seen that the balista derives its power from two arms ; each with its separate skein of cord and pair of winches.

These parts of the balista are the same in their action and mechanism as those of the catapult.

FIG. 14 (OPPOSITE PAGE). – THE MECHANISM OF THE STOCK OF AN ARROW-THROWING BALISTA.

A. Side view of the stock, with the arrow in the sliding trough before the bow-string is stretched.

B. Surface view of the stock, with the arrow in the sliding trough before the bow-string is stretched.

C. Section of the fore-end of the stock, and of the trough which slides in and along it.

---

[1] When the bow-string has been released and the arrow discharged, the ratchets are lifted clear of the cogs on the stock of the engine. This allows the trough to be slid forward to its first position as shown in A, B, Fig. 14. It is then ready to be drawn back again for the next shot.

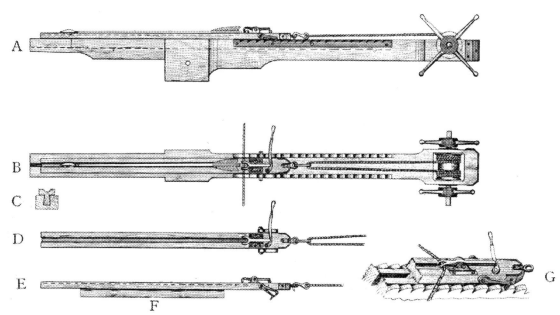

Fig. 14.—THE MECHANISM OF THE STOCK OF AN ARROW-THROWING BALISTA.

D. Surface view of the trough, with the trigger and catch for the bow-string.

E. Side view, showing the keel (F) which slides along the slot cut in the surface of the stock as the trough is drawn back by the windlass.

G. Enlarged view of the solid end of the trough. This sketch shows the catch for the bow-string, the trigger which sets it free, the ratchets which engage the cogs on the sides of the stock, and the slot cut in the stock for the dove-tailed keel of the trough to travel in.

Balistas were constructed of different sizes for the various purposes of siege and field warfare. The smallest of these engines was not much larger than a heavy crossbow, though it more than equalled the latter in power and range.

The small balistas were chiefly used for shooting through loopholes and from battlemented walls at an enemy assaulting with scaling ladders and movable towers.

The largest had arms of 3 ft. to 4 ft. in length, and skeins of twisted sinew of 6 in. to 8 in. in diameter.

Judging from models I have made and carefully experimented with, it is certain that the more powerful balistas of the ancients could cast arrows, or rather feathered javelins, of from 5 to 6 lbs. weight, to a range of from 450 to 500 yards.

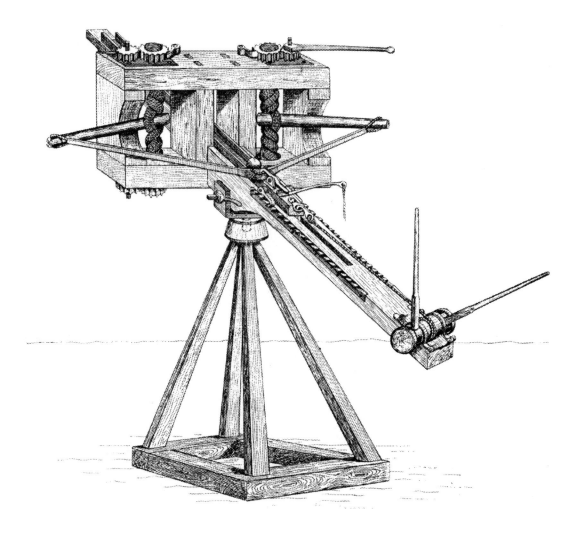

Fig.15. -- BALISTA FOR THROWING STONE BALLS. Approximate scale : ½ in.=1 foot.
This engine is here shown with its bow-string only slightly drawn along its stock by the windlass.

It will be seen that this engine is almost identical in construction with the one last described. (Fig.13.p.21)

The difference is that it propelled a stone ball instead of a large arrow.

The ball was driven along a square wooden trough, one-third of the diameter of the ball being enclosed by the sides of the trough so as to keep the missile in true direction after the bow-string was released.

The bow-string was in the form of a broad band, with an enlargement at its centre against which the ball rested.

The description given of the mechanism and management of the engine for throwing arrows can be applied to the construction and manipulation of this form of balista, which was also made of large and small dimensions.

Small engines with arms about 2 ft. in length and skeins of cord about 4 in. in diameter, such as those I have built for experiment, will send a stone ball, 1 lbs. in weight, from 300 to 350 yards.

There is little doubt that the large stone-throwing balista of the Greeks and Romans was able to project a circular stone, of 6 to 8 lbs. weight, to a distance of from 450 to 500 yards.[1]

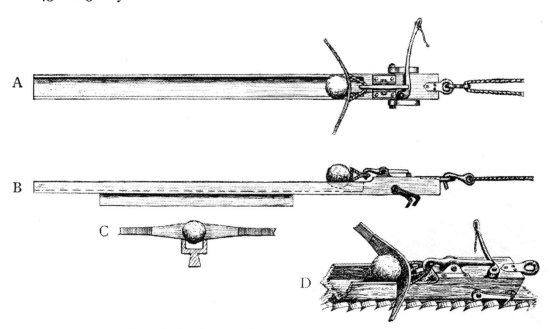

FIG. 16.-THE SLIDING TROUGH OF THE STONE-THROWING BALISTA.

A. Surface view, with the stone in position.

B. Side view, with stone in position.

C. Front view of the stone as it rests in the trough against the enlarged centre of the bow-string.

D. Enlarged view of the solid end of the sliding trough. This sketch shows the ball in position against the bow-string ; the catch bolding the loop of the bow-string, and the pivoted trigger which, when pulled, releases the catch. One of the pair of ratchets which engage the cogs on the sides of the stock, as the trough is drawn back by the windlass to make ready the engine, is also shown. The trough has a keel to it, and slides to or fro along the stock in the same manner as in the arrow-throwing balista. (Fig.13, p.21)

Compare with figs. 13, 14, pp.21, 23, for further explanation of details.

---

[1] The balls used by the ancients in their catapults and balistas were often formed of heavy pebbles inclosed in baked clay, the reason being that balls made in this way shattered on falling and hence could not be shot back by the engines of the enemy. The balistas for throwing arrows, and those employed for casting stones, were fitted with axles and wheels when constructed for use in field warfare.

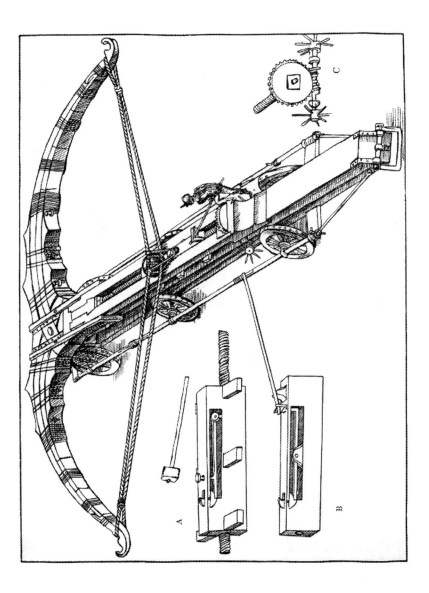

FIG 17. – A SIEGE BALISTA IN THE FORM OF AN IMMENSE STONEBOW

From 'Il Codice Atlantico,' Leonardo da Vinci, 1445 – 1520

Criticism. – A stonebow of vast size. A and B represent two kinds of lock. In A, the catch of the lock over which the loop of the bow-string was hitched, was released by striking down the knob to be seen below the mallet. In B, the catch was set free by means of a lever. C shows the manner of pulling back the bow-string. By turning the spoked wheels, the screw-worm revolved the screwed bar on which the lock A traveled. The lock, as may be seen, worked to or fro in a slot along the stock of the engine. In the illustration the bow is fully bent and the man indicated is about to discharge the engine. After this was done, the lock was wound back along the screw-bar and the bow-string was hitched over the catch of the lock preparatory to bending the bow again. Besides being a famous painter, Leonardo was distinguished as an inventor and exact writer on mechanics and hydraulics.

'No artist before his time ever had such comprehensive talents, such profound skill or so discerning a judgment to explore the depths of every art or science to which he applied himself.' – JOHN GOULD, *Dictionary of painters*, 1839.

From the above eulogy we may conclude that the drawings of ancient siege engines by Leonardo da Vinci are fairly correct.

PART IV

THE TREBUCHET

This engine was of much more recent invention than the catapult or the balista of the Greeks and Romans. It is said to have been introduced into siege operations by the French in the twelfth century. On the other hand, the catapult and the balista were in use several centuries before the Christian Era. Egidio Colonna gives a fairly accurate description of the trebuchet, and writes of it, about 1280, as though it were the most effective siege weapon of his time.

The projectile force of this weapon was obtained from the gravitation of a heavy weight, and not from twisted cordage as in the catapult and balista.

From about the middle of the twelfth century, the trebuchet in great measure superseded the catapult. This preference for the trebuchet was probably due to the fact that it was able to cast stones of about 300 lbs. in weight, or five or six times as heavy as those which the largest catapults could project.[1]

The stones thrown by the siege catapults of the time of Josephus would no doubt destroy towers and battlements, as the result of the constant and concentrated bombardment of many engines. One huge stone of from 200 to 300 lbs., as slung from a trebuchet, would, however, shake the strongest defensive masonry.

The trebuchet was essentially an engine for destroying the upper part of the walls of a fortress, so that it might be entered by means of scaling ladders or in other ways. The catapult, by reason of its longer range, was of more service in causing havoc to the people and dwelling inside the defences of a town.

From experiments with models of good size and from other sources, I find that the largest trebuchets--those with arms of about 50 ft. in length and counterpoises about 20,000 lbs.--were capable of slinging a stone from 200 to 300 lbs. in weight to a distance of 300 yards, a range of 350 yards being, in my opinion, more than these engines were able to attain.[2]

---

[1] The catapult had, besides, become an inferior engine to what it was some centuries before the trebuchet was introduced, the art of its construction having been neglected.

[2] Egidio Colonna tells us that the trebuchet was sometimes made without a counterpoise, and that in such a case the arm of the engine was worked by a number of men pulling together instead of by a heavy weight. I cannot believe this, as however many men pulled at the arm of a trebuchet they could not apply nearly the force that would be conveyed by the gravitation of a heavy weight.

FIG. 18.—THE TREBUCHET.

The arm is fully wound down and the tackle of the windlass is detached from it. The stone is in the sling and the engine is about to be discharged
by pulling the slip-hook off the end of the arm. The slip-hook is similar to the one shown in fig.10 p. 18.
N.B.--A Roman soldier is anachronistically shown in this picture. The trebuchet was invented after the time of the Romans.

The trebuchet always had a sling in which to place its missile.

The sling doubled the power of the engine and caused it to throw its projectile twice as far as it would have been able to do without it.

It was the length of the arm, when suitably weighted with its counterpoise, which combined with its sling gave power to the trebuchet. Its arm, when released, swung round with a long easy sweep and with nothing approaching the velocity of the much shorter arm of the catapult.

The weight of a projectile cast by a trebuchet was governed by the weight of its counterpoise. Provided the engine was of sufficient strength and could be manipulated, there was scarcely any limit to its power. Numerous references are to be found in mediæval authors to the practice of throwing dead horses into a besieged town with a view to causing a pestilence therein, and there can be no doubt that trebuchets alone were employed for this purpose.

As a small horse weighs about 10 cwt., we can form some idea of the size of the rocks and balls of stone that trebuchets were capable of slinging.

When we consider that a trebuchet was able to throw a horse over the walls of a town, we can credit the statement of Stella,[1] who writes ' that the Genoese armament sent against Cyprus in 1376 had among other great engines one which cast stones of 12 cwt.'

Villard de Honnecourt[2] describes a trebuchet that had a counterpoise of sand the frame of which was 12 ft. long, 8 ft. broad, and 12 ft. deep. That such machines were of vast size will readily be understood. For instance, twenty-four engines taken by Louis IX. at the evacuation of Damietta in 1249, afforded timber for stockading his entire camp.[3] A trebuchet used at the capture of Acre by the Infidels in 1291, formed a load for a hundred carts.[4] A great engine that cumbered the tower of St. Paul at Orleans and which was dismantled previous to the celebrated defence of the town against the English in 1428-9, furnished twenty-six cartloads of timber.[5]

All kinds of articles besides horses, men, stones and bombs were at times thrown from trebuchets. Vassaf[6] records 'that when the garrison of Delhi

[1] Stella flourished at the end of the fourteenth century and beginning of fifteenth. He wrote *The Annals of Genoa* from 1298-1409. Muratori includes the writing Stella in his great work, *Rerum Italicarum Scriptores*, 25 vols., 1723-38.

[2] Villard de Honnecourt, an engineer of the thirteenth century. His album translated and edited by R. Willis, MA., 1859.

[3] Jean, Sire de Joinville. He went with St. Louis to Damietta. His memoirs, written in 1309, published by F. Micheal, 1859.

[4] Abulfeda, 1273-1331. Arab soldier and historian, wrote *Annals of the Moslems*. Published by Hafnire, 1789-94 Abulfeda was himself in charge of the hundred carts.

[5] From an old history of the siege (in manuscript) found in the town hall of Orleans and printed by Saturnin Holot, a bookseller of that city, 1576.

[6] Persian historian, wrote at end of thirteen and the beginning of fourteenth century. The preface to his history is dated 1288, and the history itself is carried down to 1312.

refused to open the gates to Ala'uddin Khilji in 1296, he loaded his engines with bags of gold and shot them into the fortress, a measure which put an end to the opposition.'

Figs. 18, 20. pp.28, 32, explain the construction and working of a trebuchet.

Fig.19- CASTING A DEAD HORSE INTO A BESIEGED TOWN BY MEANS OF A TREBUCHET

From ' Il Codice Atlantico,' Leonardo da Vinci, 1445-1520

PART V

HISTORICAL NOTES ON ANCIENT AND MEDIÆVAL SIEGE ENGINES AND THEIR EFFECTS IN WARFARE

IT is evident that a history of ancient siege engines cannot be created *de novo*. All that can be done is to quote with running criticism what has been written about them.

The first mention of balistas and catapults is to be found in the Old Testament, two allusions to these weapons being made therein.

The references are :

2 Chronicles xxvii.15, 'And he[1] made in Jerusalem engines, invented by cunning men, to be on the towers and upon the bulwarks, to shoot arrows and great stones withal.'

Ezekiel xxvi. 9, 'And he shall set engines of war against thy walls'.

Through the latter extract is not so positive in its wording as the one first given, it undoubtedly refers to engines that cast either stones or arrows against the walls, especially as the prophet previously alludes to other means of assault.

One of the most authentic descriptions of the use of the great missive engines is to be found in the account by Plutarch of the siege of Syracuse by the Romans 214-212 B.C.

Cæsar in his Commentaries on the Gallic and Civil wars, B.C. 58-50, frequently mentions the engines which accompanied him in his expeditions.

The balistas on wheels were harnessed to mules and called carro-balistas.

The carro-balista discharged its heavy arrow over the head of the animal to which the shafts of the engine were attached. Among the ancients these carro-balistas acted as field artillery and one is plainly shown in use on Trajan's Column.

According to Vegetius, every cohort was equipped with one catapult and every century with one carro-balista ; eleven soldiers being required to work the latter engine.

---

[1]Uzziah.

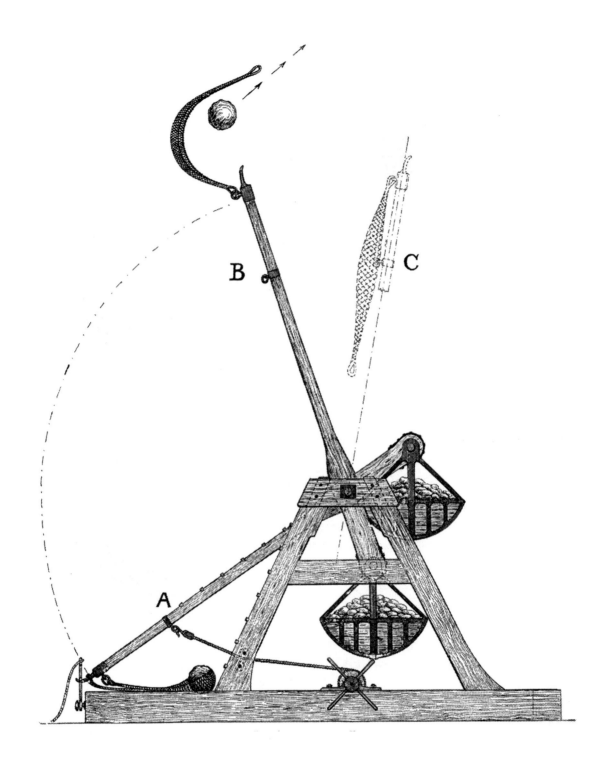

Fig. 20. -- THE ACTION OF THE TREBUCHET.

A. The arm pulled down and secured by the slip-hook previous to unhooking the rope of the windlass.   B. The arm
released from the slip-hook and casting the stone out of its sling.   C. The arm at the end of its upward sweep.

Sixty carro-balistas accompanied, therefore, besides ten catapults, a legion. The catapults were drawn along with the army on great carts yoked to oxen.

In the battles and sieges sculptured on Trajan's Column there are several figures of balistas and catapults. This splendid monument was erected in Rome, 105-113, to commemorate the victories of Trajan over the Dacians, and constitutes a pictorial record in carved stone contain some 2,500 figures of men and horses.

It is astonishing what a large number of catapults and balistas were sometimes used in a siege. For instance, at the conquest of Carthage, B.C. 146, 120 great catapults and 200 small ones were taken from the defenders, besides 33 great balistas and 52 small ones (Livy).[1]

Abulfaragio (Arab historian, 1226-1286) records that at the siege of Acre in 1191, 300 catapults and balistas were employed by Richard I. and Philip II.
Abbo, a monk of Saint German des Prés, in his poetic but very detailed account of the siege of Paris by thee Northmen in 885, 886, writes 'that the besieged had a hundred catapults on the walls of the town'.[2]

Among our earlier English King's Edward I. was the best versed in projectile weapons large and small, including crossbows and longbows.

In the Calendar of Documents relating to Scotland, an account is given of his 'War-wolf,' a siege engine in the construction of which he was much interested and which was no doubt a trebuchet.

This machine was of immense strength and size, and took fifty carpenters and five foremen a long time to complete. Edward designed it for the siege of Stirling, whither its parts were sent by land and by sea.

Sir Walter de Bedewyne, writing to a friend on July 20, 1304 (see Calendar of State Documents relating to Scotland), says : 'As for news, Stirling Castle was absolutely surrendered to the king without conditions this Monday, St. Margaret's Day, but the King wills it that none of his people enter the castle till it is struck with his "War-wolf," and that those within the castle defend themselves from the said "War-wolf" as best they can.'

From this it is evident that Edward, having constructed his 'War-wolf' to cast heavy stones into the castle of Stirling to induce its garrison to surrender was much disappointed by their capitulation before he had an opportunity of testing the power of his new weapon.

---

[1] Just previous to the famous defence of Carthage, the Carthaginians surrendered to the Romans 'two hundred thousand suits of armour and a countless number of arrows and javelins, besides catapults for shooting swift bolts and for throwing stones to the number of two thousand.' From Appian of Alexandria, a Greek writer who flourished 98-161.
[2] These were probably balistas, as Ammianus Marcellinus writes of the catapult, 'An engine of this kind placed on a stone wall shatters whatever is beneath it, not by its weight but by the violence of its shock when discharged.'

One of the last occasions on which the trebuchet was used with success is described by Guillet in his 'Life of Mahomet II.'[1] This author writes : 'At the siege of Rhodes in 1480, the Turks set up a battery of sixteen great cannon, but the Christians successfully opposed the cannon with a counterbattery of a new invention.[2]

'An engineer, aided by the most skillful carpenters in the besieged town, made an engine that cast pieces of stone of a terrible size. The execution wrought by this engine prevented the enemy from pushing forward the work of their approaches, destroyed their breastworks, discovered their mines, and filled with carnage the troops that came within range of it.'

At the siege of Mexico by Cortes in 1521, when the ammunition for the Spanish cannon ran short, a soldier with a knowledge of engineering undertook to make a trebuchet that would cause the town to surrender. A huge engine was constructed, but on its first trial the rock with which it was charged instead of flying into the town ascended straight upwards, and falling back to its starting-point destroyed the mechanism of the machine itself.[3]

Though all the projectile engines worked by cords and weights disappeared from continental warfare when cannon came to the front in a more or less improved form, they--if Vincent le Blanc is to be credited--survived in barbaric nations long after they were discarded in Europe.

This author (in his travels in Abyssinia) writes 'that in 1576 the Negus attacked Tamar, a strong town defended by high walls, and that the besieged had engines composed of great pieces of wood which were wound up by cords and screwed wheels, and which unwound with a force that would shatter a vessel, this being the cause why the Negus did not assault the town after he had dug a trench round it'.[4]

Plutarch, in his Life of Marcellus the Roman General, gives a graphic account of Archimedes and the engines this famous mathematician employed in the defence of Syracuse.

It appears that Archimedes showed his relative Hiero II., King of Syracuse, some wonderful examples of the way in which immense weights could be moved by a combination of levers.

[1] Guillet de Saint George, born about 1625, died 1705. His *Life of Mahomet II.* Was published in 1681. He was the author of several other works, including one on riding, warfare and navigation, termed the *Gentleman's Dictionary*. The best edition of this book is in English and has many very curious illustrations. It is dated 1705.
[2] Called a new invention because the old siege engine of which this one (probably a trebuchet) was a reproduction had previously been laid aside for many years.
[3] *Conquest of Mexico.* W. Prescott, 1843.
[4] Vincent le Blanc, *Voyages aux quatre parties du monde, redigé par Bergeron,* Paris,1649. Though the account given by this author of his travels are imaginative, I consider his allusion to the siege engine to be trustworthy, as he was not likely to invent so correct a description of one.

Hiero, being greatly impressed by these experiments, entreated Archimedes temporarily to employ his genius in designing articles of practical use, with the result that the scientist constructed for the king all manner of engines suitable for siege warfare.

Though Hiero did not require the machines, his reign being a peaceful one, they proved of great value shortly after his death when Syracuse was besieged by the Romans under Marcellus, 214-212. B.C.

On this occasion Archimedes directed the working of the engines he had made some years previously for Hiero.

Plutarch writes : 'And in truth all the rest of the Syracusans were no more than the body in the batteries of Archimedes, whilst he was the informing soul. All other weapons lay idle and unemployed, his were the only offensive and defensive arms of the city.'

When the Romans appeared before Syracuse, its citizens were filled with terror, for they imagined they could not possibly defend themselves against so numerous and fierce an enemy.

But, Plutarch tells us, 'Archimedes soon began to play his engines upon the Romans and their ships, and shot against them stones of such an enormous size and with so incredible a noise and velocity that nothing could stand before them. The stones overturned and crushed whatever came in their way, and spread terrible disorder through the Roman ranks. As for the machine which Marcellus brought upon several galleys fastened together, called *sambuca*[1] from its resemblance to the musical instrument of that name ; whilst it was yet at a considerable distance, Archimedes discharged at it a stone of ten talents' weight and, after that, a second stone and then a third one, all of which striking it with an amazing noise and force completely shattered it.[2]

'Marcellus in distress drew off his galleys as fast as possible and sent to his land forces to retire likewise. He then called a council of war, in

[1] *Sambuca.* A stringed instrument with cords of different lengths like a harp. The machine which Marcellus brought to Syracuse was designed to lift his soldiers--in small parties at a time and in quick succession--over the battlements of the town, so that when their numbers inside it were sufficient they might open its gates to the besiegers. The soldiers were intended to be hoisted on a platform, worked up and down by ropes and winches. As the machine was likened to a harp, it is probable it had a huge curved wooden arm fixed in an erect position and of the same shape as the modern crane used for loading vessels. If the arm of the *sambuca* had been straight like a mast, it could not have swung its load of men over a wall. Its further resemblance to a harp would be suggested by the ropes of which were employed for lifting the platform to the summit of the arm, these doubtless being fixed from the top to the foot of the engine.

[2] It is, I consider, impossible that Archimedes, however marvelous the power of his engines, was able to project a stone of ten Roman talents or nearly 600 lbs. in weight, to a considerable distance! Plutrach probably refers to the talent of Sicily, which weighed about 10 lbs. A stone of ten Sicilian talents, or say 100 lbs., could have been thrown by a catapult of great strength and size.

Though the trebuchet cast stones of from 200 lbs. to 300 lbs. and more, this weapon was not invented till long after the time of Archimedes.

which it was resolved to come close up to the walls of the city the next morning before daybreak, for they argued that the engines of Archimedes, being very powerful and designed to act at a long distance, would discharge their projectiles high over their heads. But for this Archimedes had been prepared, for he had engines at his disposal which were constructed to shoot at all ranges. When, therefore the Romans came close to the wall, undiscovered as they thought, they were assailed with showers of darts, besides huge pieces of rock which fell as it were perpendicularly upon their heads, for the engines played upon them from every quarter.

'This obliged the Romans to retire, and when they were some way from the town Archimedes used his larger machines upon them as they retreated, which made terrible havoc among them as well as greatly damaged their shipping. Marcellus, however, derided his engineers and said, "Why do we not leave off contending with this geometrical Briareus, who sitting at ease and acting as if in jest has shamefully baffled our assaults, and in striking us with such a multitude of bolts at once exceeds even the hundred-handed giant of fable?"

'At length the Romans were so terrified that, if they saw but a rope or a beam projecting over the walls of Syracuse, they cried out that Archimedes was leveling some machine at them and turned their backs and fled.'

As Marcellus was unable to control with the machines directed by Archimedes and as his ships and army had suffered severely from the effects of these stone- and javelin-casting weapons, he changed his tactics and instead of besieging the town he blockaded it and finally took it by surprise.

Though, at the time of the siege of Syracuse, Archimedes gained a reputation for divine rather than human knowledge in regard to the methods he employed in the defence of the city, he left no despription of his wonderful engines, for he regarded them as mere mechanical appliances which were beneath his serious attention, his life being devoted to solving abstruse questions of mathematics and geometry.

Archimedes was slain at the capture of Syracuse, B.C. 212, to the great regret of Marcellus.

The following extracts from Josephus, as translated by Whiston, enable us to form an excellent idea of the effects of great catapults in warfare :

(1) *Wars Of the Jews*, Book III., Chapter VII .- The siege of Jotapata, A.D 67. ' Vespasian then set the engines for throwing stones and darts round about the city ; the number of the engines was in all a hundred and sixty. . . . At the same time such engines as were intended for that purpose threw their spears buzzing forth, and stones of the weight of a talent were thrown by the engines that were prepared for doing so. . . .

'But still Josephus and those with him, although they fell down dead one upon another by the darts and stones which the engines threw upon them, did not desert the wall. . . . The engines could not be seen at a great distance and so what was thrown by them was hard to be avoided ; for the force with which these engines threw stones and darts made them wound several at a time, and the violence of the stones that were cast by the engines was so great that they carried away the pinnacles of the wall and broke off the corners of the towers ; for no body of men could be so strong as not to be overthrown to the last rank by the largeness of the stones. . . . The noise of the instruments themselves was very terrible, the sound of the darts and stones that were thrown by them was so also ; of the same sort was that noise that dead bodies made when they were dashed against the wall.'

(2) *Wars of the Jews*, Book V., Chapter VI.-- The siege of Jerusalem, A.D. 70. ' The engines that all the legions had ready prepared for them were admirably contrived ; but still more extraordinary ones belonged to the tenth legion : those that threw darts and those that threw stones were more forcible and larger than the rest, by which they not only repelled the excursions of the Jews but drove those away who were upon the walls also. Now the stones that were cast were of the weight of a talent[1] and were carried two or more stades.[2]

'The blow they gave was no way to be sustained, not only by those who stood first in the way but by those who were beyond them for a great space.

'As for the Jews, they at first watched the coming of the stone, for it was of a white colour and could therefore not only be perceived by the great noise it made, but could be seen also before it came by its brightness ; accordingly the watchmen that sat upon the towers gave notice when an engine was let go. . . .
so those that were in its way stood off and threw themselves down upon the ground. But the Romans contrived how to prevent this by blacking the stone ; they could then aim with success when the stone was not discerned beforehand, as it had been previously.'

The accounts given by Josephus are direct and trustworthy evidence, for the reason that this chronicler relates what he personally witnessed during the sieges he describes, in one of which (Jotapata) he acted the part of a brave and resourceful commander.

Tacitus in describing a battle fought near Cremona between the armies of Vitellius and Vespasian, A.D. 69, writes : ' The Vitellians at this time changed the position of their battering-engines, which in the beginning were placed in different parts of the field and could only play at random against the woods and hedges that sheltered the enemy. They were now moved to

---

[1]   57 3/4 lbs.. (avoirdupois).
[2]   Two stades would be 404 yards ; the measure of a stade is 606 3/4 English feet.

The Postumian way, and thence having an open space before them could discharge, their missiles with good effect.'[1]

Froissart chronicles that at the siege of Thyn-l'Evêque,1340, in the Low Countries, 'John, Duke of Normandy had a great abundance of engines carted from Cambrai and Douai Among the others he had six very large ones which he placed before the fortress, and which day and night cast great stones which battered in the tops on the roofs of the towers and of the rooms and halls, so much so that the men who defended the place took refuge in the cellars and vaults.'

Camden records that the strength of the engines employed for throwing stones was incredibly great and that with the engines called mangonels[2] they used to throw millstones. Camden adds that when King John laid siege to Bedford Castle, there were on the east side of the castle two catapults battering the old tower, as also two upon the south side besides another on the north side which beat two breaches in the walls.

The same authority asserts that when Henry III. was besieging Kenilworth Castle, the garrison had engines which cast stones of a extraordinary size, and that near the castle several balls of stones sixteen inches in diameter have been found which are supposed to have been thrown by engines with slings[3] in the time of the Barons' war.

Holinshed writes that ' when Edward I attacked Stirling Castle, he caused an engine of wood to be set up to batter the castle which shot stones of two or three hundredweight.' (See allusion to this, pg. 33)

Père Daniel, in his *Histoire de la Milice Françoise*, writes : ' The great object of the French engineers was to make siege of sufficient strength to project stones large enough to crush the roofs of houses and break down the walls.' This author continues : 'The French engineers were so successful and cast stones of such enormous size that their missiles even penetrated the vaults and floors of the most solidly built houses.'[4]

The effects of the balista on the defenders of a town were in no degree inferior to those of the catapult. The missile of the balista consisted of a huge metal-tipped wooden bolt which, although of far less weight than the great ball of stone cast by a catapult or the far larger one thrown by a trebuchet, was

---

[1] Tacitus continues : 'The fifteenth legion had an engine of enormous size, which was played off with dreadful execution and discharge massy stones of a weight to crush whole ranks at once. Inevitable ruin must have followed if two soldiers had not signalised themselves by a brave exploit. Covering themselves with shields of the enemy which they found among the slain, they advanced undiscovered to the battering-engine and cut its ropes and springs. In this bold adventure they both perished and with them two names that deserved to be immortal.'

[2] Catapults were often called mangons or mangonels, but in course of time the name magonel was applied to any siege engine that projected stones or arrows. In this case the trebuchet is intended, as no catapult could project a millstone.

[3] The engines here alluded to by Camden were trebuchets.

[4] These engines would also be trebuchets.

able to penetrate roofs and cause great destruction in ranks of soldiers. Cæsar records that when his lieutenant Caius Trebonius was building a moveable tower at the siege of Marseilles, the only method of protecting the workmen from the darts of engines[1] was by hanging curtains woven from cable-ropes on the three sides of the tower exposed to the besiegers.[2]

Procopius relates that during the siege of Rome in 537 by Vitiges King of Italy, he saw a Gothic chieftain in armour suspended to a tree which he had climbed, and to which he had bee nailed by a balista bolt which had passed through his body and then penetrated into the tree behind him.

Again, at the siege of Paris by the Northmen in 885-886, Abbo writes that Ebolus[3] discharged from a balista a bolt which transfixed several of the enemy.

With grim humour Ebolus bade their comrades carry the slain to the kitchen, his suggestion being that the men impaled on the shaft of the balista resembled fowls run through with a spit previous to being roasted.

Not only were ponderous balls of stone and heavy bolts projected into a town and against its walls and their defenders, but, with a view to causing a pestilence, it was also the custom to throw in dead horses, and even the bodies of soldiers who had been killed in sorties or assaults.

For example, Varillas[4] writes that 'at his ineffectual siege of Carolstein in 1422, Coribut caused the bodies of his solders whom the besieged had killed to be thrown into the town in addition to 2,000 cartloads of manure. A great numbers of the defenders fell victims to the fever which resulted from the stench, and the remainder were only saved from death by the skill of a rich apothecary who circulated in Carolstein remedies against the poison which infected the town.'

Froissart tells us that at the siege of Auberoche, an emissary who came to treat for terms was seized and shot back into town. This author writes :

'To make it more serious, they took the varlet and hung the letters around his neck and instantly placed him in the sling of an engine and then shot him back again into Auberoche. The varlet arrived dead before the knights who were there and who were much astonished and discomfited when they saw him arrive.'

Another historian explains that to shoot a man from the sling of an engine he must first be tied up with the ropes, so as to form a round bundle like a sack of grain.

The engine with which such fiendish deeds were achieved was the trebuchet.

---

[1] Balistas

[2] 'For this was the only sort of defence which they had learned, by experience in other places, could not be pierced by darts or engines'. Cæsar's *Commentaries on the Civil War*, Book II., Chapter IX.

[3] Abbot of Saint-Germain des Prés and one of the chief defenders of the town.

[4] French historian, born 1624, died 1696.

A catapult was not powerful enough to project the body of a man. This difficulty was overcome by cutting off the head of any unfortunate emissary for peace, if the terms he brought were scornfully rejected. His letter of supplication from the besieged was then nailed to his skull, and his head was sent flying through space to fall inside the town as a ghastly form of messenger conveying a refusal to parley.

As it was always an object to the besiegers of a town to start a conflagration if they could, Greek fire was used for the purpose. The flame of this fearfully destructive liquid, the composition of which is doubtful, could not be quenched by water. It was placed in round earthenware vessels that broke on falling, and which were shot from catapults ; as the roofs of ancient and mediæval dwelling-houses were usually thatched, it of coarse dealt destruction when it encountered such combustible material.

The successful attack or defence of a fortified town often depended on which of the armies engaged had the more powerful balistas, catapults or trebuchets, as one engine of superior range could work destruction unimpeded if it happened that a rival of similar power was not available to check its depredations.

Froissart relates that 'at the siege of Mortagne in 1340, an engineer within the town constructed an engine to keep down the discharges of one powerful machine in the besieging lines. At the third shot he was so lucky as to break the arm of the attacking engine.' The account of this incident, as given by Froissart, is so quaint and graphic that I quote it here : ' The same day they of Valencens raysed on their syde a great engyn and dyd cast in stones so that it troubled sore them within the town. Thus ye first^e day passed and the night in assayling and devysing how they might greve them in the fortress.

'Within Mortagne there was a connying maister in making of engyns who saw well how the engyn of Valencens did greatly greve them : he raysed an engyn in ye castle, the which was not very great but he trymmed it to a point,[1] and he cast therwith but three tymes. The firste stone fell a xii[2] fro the engyn without, the second fell on ye engyn, and the thirde stone hit so true that it brake clene asonder the shaft the engyn without ; then the soldyers of Mortagne made a great shout, so that the Hainaulters could get nothing ther[3] ; then the erle[4] sayd how he wolde withdrawe.'

(From the translation made at the request of Henry VII, by John Bourchier, second Lord Berners, published 1523-1525.)

---

[1] *i.e.* with great exactness or 'to a hair'.   [2] A foot
[3] Could not throw any more stones.
[4] Count of Hainault. He was besieging Tournay, but left that place and went to besiege Mortagne and ordered the people of Valenciennes to go with him.

These siege engines when only of moderate size were not always successful, as in some cases the walls of a town were so massively built that the projectiles of the enemy made little impression upon them. Froissart tells us that it was then the habit of the defenders of the walls to pull off their caps, or produce cloths, and derisively dust the masonry when it was struck by stones.

Some of the historians, mechanicians and artist from whom information on balistas, catapults and trebuchets may be derived are as follows. I name them alphabetically irrespective of their periods :

ABBO : A monk of Saint-Germain des Prés, born about the middle of the ninth century, died in 923. He wrote a poem in Latin describing the siege of Paris by the Northmen in 885-886.

AMMIANUS MARCELLINUS : Military historian. Died shortly after 390. His work first printed at Rome 1474. The latest edition is that of V. Gardthausen, 1874-1875.

APPIAN : Historian. Lived at Rome during the reigns of Trajan, Hadrian and Antoninus Pius, 98-161. The best edition of his History is that of Schweighaeuser, 1785.

APOLLODORUS OF DAMASCUS : Built Trajan's Column, 105-113. Architect and engineer. Addressed a series of letters to the Emperor Trajan on siege engines (*vide* Thévenot).

ATHENÆUS : Lived in the time of Archimedes, B.C. 287-212. The author of a treatise on warlike engines (*vide* Thévenot).

BITON : Flourished about 250 B.C. Wrote a treatise on siege engines for throwing stones (*vide* Thévenot).

BLONDEL, FRANÇOIS : French engineer and architect ; born 1617 ; died 1686.

CÆSAR, JULIUS (the Dictator) : Born B.C. 100 ; died B.C. 44 Author of the 'Commentaries' on the Gallic and Civil wars.

CAMDEN, WILLIAM : Born 1551 ; died 1623. Antiquary. Published his 'Britannia' 1586-1607.

COLONNA, EGIDIO : Died 1316. Archbishop of Bourges 1294, after having been tutor to Philip the Fair of France. His best known works are 'Quæstiones Metaphysicales' and 'De Regimine Principum' ; the latter was written about 1280. Colonna gives a description of the siege engines of his time.

DANIEL, PÈRE GABRIEL : Historian. Born 1649 ; died 1728.

DIODORUS (the Sicilian) : Historian. Lived under Julius and Augustus Cæsar (Augustus died A.D. 14). The best modern edition is that edited by L. Dindorf, 1828.

FABRETTI, RAFFAEL : Antiquary.   Born 1618 ; died 1700.

FROISSART, JEAN : French chronicler. Born about 1337 ; died 1410. His Chronicles printed about 1500. Translated into English by Lord Berners, and published 1523-1525.

GROSE, FRANCIS : Military historian and antiquary. Born about 1731 ; died 1791. Published 'Military Antiquities' 1786-1788.

HERON OF ALEXANDRIA : Mechanician. Lived B.C. 284-221. Benardino Baldi edited his work on arrows and siege engines, 1616 (*vide* Thévenot).

ISIDORUS, BISHOP OF SEVILLE : Historian. Died 636.

JOSEPHUS, FLAVIUS : Jewish historian. Born A.D. 37 ; died about the year 100. Wrote the 'History of the Jewish Wars' and also 'Jewish Antiquties.' Josephus, acting as commander of the besieged, bravely defened Jotapata A.D. 67, against the Roman general Vespasian. He was also present with the Roman army during the siege of Jerusalem by Titus, A.D. 70.

LEONARDO DA VINCI : Italian painter. Born 1445 : died 1520. In the immense volume of sketches and MSS. By this famous artist, which is preserved at Milan and entitled 'IL Codice Atlantico,' there are several drawings of siege engines.

LIPSIUS, JUSTUS : Historian. Born 1547 ; died 1606.

MEZERAY, FRANCOIS E. DE : French historian. Born 1610 ; died 1683. Published 'Histoire de France,' 1643-1651.

NAPOLEON III.: 'Etudes sur l'artillerie,' complied by order of the Emperor and containing many drawings of the full sized models of siege engines made by his orders, with interesting and scientific criticism of their power and effect.

PHILO OF BYZANTIUM : A writer on and inventor of warlike and other engines. Lived shortly after the time of Archimedes (Archimedes died 212 B.C.) : was a contemportary of Ctesibius, who lived in the reign of Ptolemy Physcon, B.C.. 170-117 (*vide* Thévenot).

PLUTARCH : Biographer and historian. Time and birth and death unknown. He was a young man in A.D. 66.

POLYBIUS : Military historian. Born about B.C. 204. His History commences B.C. 220 and concludes B.C. 146. The most interesting edition is the one translated into French by Vincent Thuiller with a commentary by de Folard, 1727-1730.

PROCOPIUS : Byzantine historian. Born about 500 ; died 565, the best edition is that of L. Dindorf, 1833-1838.

FIG. 21.--THE CAPTURE OF A FORTRESS.

Criticism.-A fortification being entered by the besiegers, who have made a breach in the outside wall with a battering ram.

A catapult is in the corner of the picture, and four men are taking a balista up the approach to the gateway.

From Polybius. Edition 1727.

RAMELLI, AGOSTINO : Italian engineer. Born about 1531 : died 1590. Published a work on projectile and other engines, 1588.

TACITUS, CORNELIUS : Roman historian, Born about A.D. 61.

THÉVENOT, MELCHISEDECH : 1620-1692 : Edited a book called 'The Mathematici Veteres,' containing several treatises on the siege operations of the ancients including the construction and management of their projectile engines. In this book are to be found the writings on the subject of military engines that were complied by Athenæus, Apolloddorus, Biton, Heron and Philo. Thévenot was the King's librarian to Louis XIV. After his death the manuscript of 'Mathematici Veteres,' or the 'The Ancient Mathematicians' was revised and published by La Hire in 1693. The book was again edited by Boivin, an official in the King's library, who lived 1663-1726. The treatises contained in Thévenot were finally re-edited and published by C. Wescher, Paris, 1869.

VALTURIUS, ROBERTUS : Military author. Living at the end of the fifteenth century. His book ' De Re Militari' first printed at Verona, 1472.

VEGETIUS, FLAVIUS RENATUS : Roman military writer. Flourished in the time of the Emperor Valentinian II., 375-392. The best edition is that of Schwebel, 1767.

VIOLLET-LE-DUC : French military historian. Published his 'Dictionnaire raisonné de l'Architecture,' 1861.

VITRUVIUS POLLIO : architect and military engineer and inspector of military engines under the Emperor Augustus. Born between B.C. 85 and 75. His tenth book treats of siege engines. Translated into French with commentary by Perrault, 1673. The most interesting editions of Vitruvius are those containing the commentary on siege engines by Philander. The best of these is dated 1649.

Printed in the United States
69410LVS00006B/134